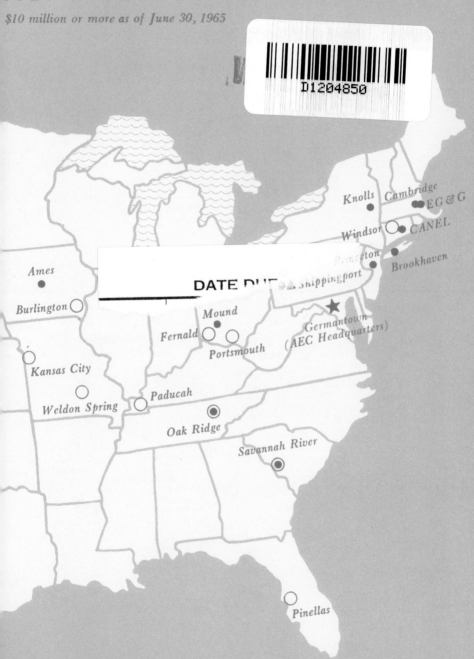

Knolls Cambridge EG&G

Windsor CANEL

Princeton Brookhaven

Shippingport

Germantown
(AEC Headquarters)

Ames

Burlington

Mound

Fernald

Kansas City Portsmouth

Weldon Spring Paducah

Oak Ridge

Savannah River

Pinellas

(▲ Puerto Rico)

CONTRACTING
FOR ATOMS

CONTRACTING FOR ATOMS

HAROLD ORLANS

A study of public policy issues
posed by the Atomic Energy Commission's contracting
for research, development, and managerial services

The Brookings Institution · Washington, D.C.

© 1967 by

THE BROOKINGS INSTITUTION
1775 Massachusetts Avenue, N.W.
Washington, D.C.

Published February 1967

Library of Congress Catalogue Card Number 67-17131

THE BROOKINGS INSTITUTION is an independent organization devoted to nonpartisan research, education, and publication in
economics, government, foreign policy, and the social sciences
generally. Its principal purposes are to aid in the development of sound public policies and to promote public understanding of issues of national importance.

The Institution was founded December 8, 1927, to merge the activities of
the Institute for Government Research, founded in 1916, the Institute of
Economics, founded in 1922, and the Robert Brookings Graduate School of
Economics and Government, founded in 1924.

The general administration of the Institution is the responsibility of a
self-perpetuating Board of Trustees. The trustees are likewise charged with
maintaining the independence of the staff and fostering the most favorable
conditions for creative research and education. The immediate direction of
the policies, program, and staff of the Institution is vested in the President,
assisted by the division directors and an advisory council, chosen from the
professional staff of the Institution.

In publishing a study, the Institution presents it as a competent treatment
of a subject worthy of public consideration. The interpretations and conclusions in such publications are those of the author or authors and do not purport to represent the views of the other staff members, officers, or trustees of
the Brookings Institution.

Foreword

This study is concerned with public policy issues posed by the Atomic Energy Commission's contracting with private organizations for research and development and for the management of government-owned nuclear plants and laboratories. The inquiry has been conducted entirely under disinterested private auspices, as part of a broader study of government contracting policy supported by a grant from the Carnegie Corporation. Clarence H. Danhof has been responsible for that broader study which, like the present one, has been conducted under the general direction of George A. Graham, Director of Governmental Studies at Brookings.

Special thanks are due to Commission Chairman Glenn T. Seaborg and to Commissioner James T. Ramey for facilitating the present study, and to AEC headquarters and regional staff who contributed detailed comments and corrections on a draft circulated in June 1965. That draft also provoked an unusual amount of comment from private authorities on nuclear affairs, to whom we are most grateful.

In keeping with normal practice, the manuscript was reviewed by a reading committee, whose comments were unusually helpful. It consisted of Don K. Price, Dean of the Graduate School of Public Administration, Harvard University; Wallace S. Sayre, Professor of Public Law and Government, Columbia University; and Frederick C. Schuldt, Jr., Assistant Chief for Atomic Energy, Bureau of the Budget.

As this book discusses a number of issues about which reasonable, informed, and responsible men may well disagree, it may be appropriate to note that, by publishing a study, the Brookings

Institution does not take any position on the views it contains. The views expressed in this book are those of the author, and do not purport to represent the views of the reading committee, the AEC, the Carnegie Corporation, or of other staff members, officers, or trustees of the Brookings Institution.

ROBERT D. CALKINS
President

October 1966
Washington, D. C.

Author's Preface

The present inquiry has been based upon well over 100 interviews with officials at AEC headquarters and regional offices, contractor personnel, and others knowledgeable about nuclear affairs; public documents; and a considerable volume of private communications. Interviews were conducted intermittently from October 1962 to January 1966, but were concentrated mainly in the first six months of 1964 and, unless otherwise specified, the general time horizon pertains to the same period. However, for additional perspective, pertinent historical material drawn from the public record of the last twenty-five years has also been included, particularly in Part II, "Dramatis Personae," which describes some of the major actors on the nuclear stage who have been responsible for the AEC's performance to date—insofar as anyone may be held responsible. The nuclear drama itself has been so extraordinary that, while the actors are manifestly human and their words manifest not only a conscious but, at times, a singular intelligence, one cannot shed a feeling that the script has been written by no human hand. The ultimate purpose for which some of the ablest scientists, industrialists, and political leaders of our time have been sifting and assembling elemental forces remains uncertain.

The investigation has been conducted throughout on an unclassified basis. AEC and private officials were uniformly cooperative and, in most cases, candid. I was, indeed, surprised and impressed to find those responsible for such deadly secrets so frank and open in discussing their policies and problems. Failures in communication must be attributed more to my level of understanding than to informants' unwillingness to raise it. In twenty years of research, I have not before encountered such a thirst for disclosure, and I believe that it has a certain public significance. I may be mistaken, but I think it signifies a wish to break the circle of privacy and isolation from the arena of public political discourse that has too long circumscribed the nation's nuclear affairs. The days when utter secrecy was needed have passed, but the institutions and habits bred in those days have not.

A word may be in order about the extensive use of anonymous quotations, since, though the maintenance of confidence is essential, upon occasion, to government officials, social scientists, and persons in most walks of life, there are some in Washington who, while reserving the right of confidence for themselves, would deny it to scholars.

All informants, who included some of the most respected figures in national nuclear affairs, were pledged anonymity, and that pledge has been honored. Many authorities from both older and newer professions might be cited in defense of the obligation to preserve confidence in social research. A recent article, "Privacy and Behavioral Research," by a lawyer and a sociologist, observes:

The integrity of the professional scientist will assure both his informants and society at large that he will be responsible and will maintain the confidence of any information given to him by identifiable informants. . . .

It is generally accepted that research data should not be published by the investigator with identities of the individual subject attached. . . . Thus, it should be part of the responsibility of the research scientist not to make his research data, in which individuals are identifiable, available to others, whether such others be . . . journalists, government agents, or even other scientists.*

The accuracy of quotations drawn from interviews has, in most cases, been checked by referral to the person interviewed; other quotations are drawn from private communications from persons qualified to speak about the matter at hand. While the accuracy of this material can, accordingly, be vouched for, the same claim cannot be made for its validity.

* Oscar M. Ruebhausen (Chairman of the Special Committee on Science and Law of the Association of the Bar of the City of New York) and Orville G. Brim, Jr. (President, Russell Sage Foundation), in *Columbia Law Review* (November 1965), pp. 1205, 1207.

Some may regard anonymity as a form of irresponsibility, and it is admittedly difficult to know what weight should be placed on a remark without knowing its author and the circumstances that evoked it. However, as an anonymous spokesman receives neither blame *nor* credit, he may state his views with special frankness and honesty. To the extent that this is true (and if I did not believe that my informants were honest, I would not have repeated what they said), anonymous judgment serves the only purpose for which it is here presented—opening issues for public discussion. It need not also constitute an adequate basis for the determination of public policy; for this more serious purpose, men should doubtless stand up and be counted as they do at congressional hearings— or in the advice they give privately to public officials!

A few comments on the origins of the various sections of this book may make their purpose clearer to the reader.

Part I, which deals most explicitly with AEC contract policies, stood initially by itself, and remains the section in which most of the fresh empirical information gathered in the study is reported.

Having read it, my colleagues at Brookings felt that a description of the major groups involved in these high and middling contractual matters was lacking, and asked that it be supplied. Part II was my effort to do so. Written more from library than from field sources—that is, from secondary rather than primary materials—it is not and does not pretend to be an original contribution to knowledge, and those familiar with the still somewhat cloistered world of atomic energy may prefer to skip it.

The final chapter is devoted to two larger issues: the AEC's role in high energy physics and the future of the agency. Both issues go beyond the initial scope of the study, but emerged directly from it. After the smaller points of contractual policy had been discussed, informants often dwelt on such larger questions, and it would be irresponsible not to indicate what they were.

In addition to the commissioners and the members of the reading committee cited by President Calkins in his foreword, I want also to express my thanks to Dwight Ink, James Scammahorn, and Hugo Eskildson for repeated, patient, and valuable assistance; to Brigadier General Delmar Crowson, Clarence Ohlke, John Ryan, and James Yore for special information; and to many other members of the AEC staff who cannot be named because their lengthy and helpful comments were transmitted by the AEC anonymously. AEC's staff struck me as a group of exceptionally able men, who discharge their exceptional responsibilities with exceptional devotion, hard work, and meticulousness.

Indispensable as were the contributions of AEC staff, the contributions of authorities in other government agencies, private organizations, and private life were, if possible, even more indispensable. Without holding them in any way accountable for my errors of omission or commission, I want to single out for thanks the following significant minority of those who conveyed detailed comments on the draft of this book or were helpful in other ways during the study: Robert Barlow, Ralph D. Bennett, Guy Black, Richard D. Bokum II, Lawrence R. Caruso, W. J. Catacosinos, Gerald Charnoff, John T. Conway, Albert V. Crewe, Lauchlin M. Currie, Lee A. DuBridge, Charles E. Falk, S. L. Fawcett, H. A. Fidler, John S. Foster, James Grant, Harold P. Green, General Leslie R. Groves, Lawrence R. Hafstad, William B. Harrell, Frederic de Hoffmann, Warren C. Johnson, Wilfrid E. Johnson, Arnold Kramish, Leonard L. Lederman, J. P. Lyon, Bernard J. O'Keefe, Loren K. Olson, Edwin M. McMillan, Wolfgang K. H. Panofsky, H. M. Parker, Donald L. Peyton, William G. Pollard, David Z. Robinson, S. P. Schwartz, Henry D. Smyth, David T. Stanley, Chauncey Starr, Admiral Lewis L. Strauss, James E. Webb, Alvin M. Weinberg, and Daniel M. Wilkes. Eugene Latimer and the Board of Directors of the Federal Bar Association kindly made available a tape recording of a discussion of AEC contract policies at the Association's 1963 Annual Convention. And one anonymous commentator presented such a trenchant analysis of the present status and objectives of the nuclear "dramatis personae" that it has been reproduced verbatim in an appendix (see pp. 203-08).

At the Brookings Institution, George Graham, Director of Governmental Studies, provided invaluable, steadfast support throughout considerable vicissitudes; it is simple honesty to say that without his support this study would not have been completed. Clarence Danhof, who has been responsible for the overall study of government contracting policy, and George Wright, who was associated with it for some years, have been constantly helpful colleagues. Miss Janet Porter performed the secretarial duties with unusual ability and has materially contributed to the textual accuracy. Mrs. Patricia Natirbov has been a tolerant and expeditious editor. Mrs. Florence Robinson prepared the index.

None of the persons named, or the larger number of informants and readers who remain unnamed, and none of the officers or staff of the Atomic Energy Commission, the Brookings Institution, or the Carnegie Corporation is responsible for the choice of material or for the opinions and conclusions presented in this book, which are solely the responsibility of the author.

HAROLD ORLANS

October 1966
Washington, D. C.

Contents

PART I

Contract Policies—and Practices

CHAPTER I

New Technology by Contract

On January 1, 1947, the Atomic Energy Commission[1] inherited the property and responsibilities of the Army's Manhattan Engineer District, including the most deadly fruit plucked from the tree of knowledge since Genesis. In the ensuing years through June 1966, the Commission spent some $38.6 billion sustaining, improving, enlarging, and diversifying the enterprise in which the Army had invested $2.2 billion. In more recent years, its annual operating and capital budget has approximated $2.6 billion. Its consumption of electric power, most of which is required for uranium enrichment, rose from 5.5 billion kilowatt-hours in 1951 to a peak of 60.7 billion killowatt-hours in 1956,[2] then 12 percent

[1] Henceforth referred to, also, as "the AEC" or "the Commission." The governing body of the agency (composed of five Commissioners appointed by the President with the consent of the Senate, one of whom is designated by the President as Chairman) may also be referred to as "the Commission," since in principle, the policies of a majority of the Commissioners are also those of the entire agency. Where it becomes important to refer solely to the group of five men, reference may be made to "the Commissioners." Commissioners are appointed for a five year term or for the unexpired portion of an incomplete term.

[2] The Manhattan Engineer District disbursed $858.6 million in fiscal year 1945; in fiscal year 1953, the Atomic Energy Commission received $1.1 billion regular and $3.0 billion supplemental appropriations, of which $3.4 billion was for new plant and equipment. *Atomic Energy Legislation Through 88th Congress, 1st session,* Joint Committee on Atomic Energy, 88 Cong. 1 sess. (December 1963), pp. 237, 277, 278. Regarding power consumption, see Philip Mullenbach, *Civilian Nuclear Power* (Twentieth Century Fund, New York, 1963), pp. 124-25; and *Chemical and Engineering*

of the nation's total. This prodigious effort has yielded a stockpile estimated by one magazine at over 30,000 nuclear and hydrogen bombs in 1963;[3] the technology for the nuclear propulsion of ninety-two submarines and four naval surface ships (authorized as of March 1965); a broad program of fundamental research in physics, chemistry, metallurgy, biology, medicine, and other fields; and major programs to develop new ways of generating electricity, of propelling planes, missiles, and rockets, and of using nuclear processes for other military and civilian purposes.

The AEC might be briefly characterized as an agency that, originating primarily as a weaponeer for the military, has gradually assumed major research and development (R&D) functions in a broad spectrum of civilian as well as military nuclear technology and science. However, unlike the R&D agencies of the three armed services and the National Aeronautics and Space Administration (with each of which it has important coordinated programs), the AEC has operated none of its laboratories with government personnel, but solely by contract with private organizations.[4] This has been a deliberate policy, for the AEC was not,

---

News (Dec. 17, 1956), p. 6161. In the spring of 1964, when the diffusion plants were operating at a 5250 megawatt level, power cuts of 40 percent were announced.

[3] *Time* has stated that "The actual number [of nuclear warheads, tactical and strategic] may be reckoned with reasonable accuracy at some 33,000 warheads on station; or held, carefully stored, in ready reserve; or otherwise committed to the arsenal. Another 15,000 are in preparation." (Aug. 23, 1963), p. 11. A number of other published sources gives estimates in the same order of magnitude.

[4] With three small but interesting exceptions: The AEC operated a laboratory in Winchester, Mass., for assaying raw materials, which has been closed out; and maintains an analytical control laboratory at New Brunswick, N. J., and a health control laboratory in New York City. With regard to the former, the manager of the Commission's New York office has stated: "Since pricing frequently depends on the attainment of precise purity standards or upon uranium content of ores and since product analysis offers an opportunity for evaluation of contractor performance, it was believed that such judgment could not rightly be delegated to another contractor but should instead be made directly by the Government." His explanation of the reasons for the Commission's operation of the latter laboratory is somewhat less convincing: "Because many of the New York Operations Office contractors are relatively small, highly specialized firms that would not be able to maintain economically the necessary equipment and personnel, a health control group has been set up in the New York Headquarters. An Instrument Development Laboratory and a Radiological Laboratory, including radon counting, spectrographic and fluorometric apparatus for the determination of radium, uranium, or beryllium in breath or biological samples, and other general analytical facilities are maintained . . ." If these reasons were com-

like the National Science Foundation, proscribed by statute from operating its own laboratories; on the contrary, one avowed purpose of the Atomic Energy Act of 1946 was to provide for "A Program of *federally* conducted research and development. . . ."[5] This self-denying policy was the more remarkable in view of the unprecedented and exclusive powers given by this act to the AEC to own all fissionable material and all facilities for its production, and to license and control its distribution and use.

The policy represented a continuation by the peacetime commission of the basic wartime policy of General Leslie Groves and the Manhattan Project, that contracting with a few of the nation's largest and best qualified companies and universities was the most expeditious and effective way to develop, design, and produce atomic bombs. There were occasions during the war when direct government operation of a vital installation such as the Los Alamos laboratory was considered; and there can be little doubt that, had circumstances required (if, for example, critical work had been interrupted by a strike or sabotage), government intervention would have occurred and may still occur. However, the permanent government operation of major installations was never favored by a majority of the Commission or the Congress, for several reasons:

1. Most of the key industrialists and scientists opposed it, believing that military or civil service management would be less effective than that of a private organization, and would handicap recruitment of the best people. Whether they were right or wrong, as a matter of general principle, was less relevant than the historical fact that extraordinary technical and industrial virtuosity had been displayed, and the bombs *had* been built under this policy. Why change a successful policy?

---

pelling, one would expect the Commission to operate a chain of such laboratories to serve clusters of small nuclear firms in other regions. (See Wilbur E. Kelley, "Contract Policies and Procedures, New York Operations Office," *Atomic Energy Industrial and Legal Problems*, University of Michigan Law School, Ann Arbor, 1952, p. 133.)

[5] Atomic Energy Act of 1946. Sec. 1(b)(3); our italics. Sec. 3(b) reads further: "Research by the Commission. The Commission is authorized and directed to conduct, through its own facilities, activities and studies of the types specified. . . ." Sec. 4(c)(2) states: "The Commission is authorized and directed to produce or to provide for the production of fissionable material in its own facilities."

Consideration was once given to making Los Alamos a military laboratory. This is worth recalling for the insight it affords into the scientists' aversion to bureaucratic, and particularly military, management—i.e., to pursuing the truth by normal hierarchical channels of authority:

The assumption at the outset was that Los Alamos would be a military laboratory. The narrowly martial, supersecret mission appeared to demand it. . . . Oppenheimer went along with the idea and even visited the Presidio in San Francisco to take the first steps toward becoming a commissioned officer. . . . According to plans, the director would be perhaps a lieutenant colonel and the heads of the scientific divisions majors. . . .

The events that frustrated these plans and assured the civilian character of Los Alamos began with Oppenheimer's efforts at recruiting. . . . He wanted particularly to enlist Robert F. Bacher and Isidor I. Rabi, two outstanding physicists in the Radiation Laboratory at MIT. . . . Bacher and Rabi feared that a military laboratory could accomplish nothing significant . . . military organization would introduce a dangerous rigidity. Would not an Army officer find it difficult to be wrong, to change a decision? What assurance was there that he would act on scientific grounds?

. . . Bacher answered the call to Los Alamos with a letter of acceptance which he stated was also his resignation, effective the day the laboratory became a military installation. . . . Groves never acted on the plans to militarize.[6]

2. The 1946 Atomic Energy Act already gave the government monopolistic and in some respects draconian powers (the phrase "shall . . . be punished by death" recurs a good many times), abrogating in the nuclear field traditional rights of private ownership, private patents, and the free exchange of information. Contracting with private organizations for the management, staffing, and operation of government-owned plants and laboratories was the principal remaining means of retaining a degree of normalcy and freedom in the evolving system of nuclear science and industry.

[6] Richard G. Hewlett and Oscar E. Anderson, Jr., *The New World, 1939/1946* (Pennsylvania State University Press, University Park, 1962), pp. 230-32. A well placed witness asserted in 1965 that there were not so much specific "plans to militarize" as a readiness to do so should it prove desirable; in the process, Oppenheimer was given a physical examination to see if he could qualify as an officer.

Although Sec. 4 of S. 1717, as introduced by Senator McMahon in December 1945, required existing contracts for the production of fissionable material to be continued for no more than one year, within which time the AEC would "arrange for the exclusive operation of the facilities . . . by employees of the Commission,"[7] this provision was dropped from the final act, which prescribed exclusive government ownership of the facilities but authorized the Commission "to make, or to continue in effect, contracts with persons obligating them to produce fissionable material in facilities owned by the Commission."

However, the act also prohibited the Division of Research from supporting research by private agencies,[8] the intention being to have it operate its own laboratory—which it noticeably did not do. James Newman thereupon complained that the Commission had "stripped [the Division] . . . of functions contemplated by Congress"; that the Commission's policy "of conducting research exclusively by contract . . . seems . . . an improper evasion of responsibilities clearly fixed in the Act"; and that "the preference shown by Congress for the maximum safe participation of private industry in atomic matters has been interpreted by the AEC as a dogma . . . the Commission has elevated private participation above every other principle except possibly security."[9] But neither the Congress nor the first Commission (four of whose five members were Republicans)[10] or their successors were disposed to contest this principle or risk disrupting a going enterprise for the uncertain advantages of government operation:

In 1947, the atomic energy facilities entrusted to the Commission

[7] Hewlett and Anderson, *op. cit.*, p. 494.

[8] Sec. 2(a)(4)(B) of the 1946 Atomic Energy Act prohibited the Division of Research from contracting for research and development, as the three other statutory divisions were permitted to do under Sec. 3(a) of the Act. This portion of Sec. 2(a)(4)(B) was eliminated on July 31, 1953, by Public Law 164, 83 Cong., so that, upon determination by the Commission, all divisions were able to contract for R&D. See *Atomic Energy Legislation Through 88th Congress, 1st Session,* Joint Committee on Atomic Energy (December 1963), p. 207, footnote 4.

[9] See James R. Newman and Byron S. Miller, *The Control of Atomic Energy* (McGraw-Hill, New York, 1948), footnotes on pp. 37 and 187; and James R. Newman, "The Atomic Energy Industry," *Yale Law Journal* (December 1951), pp. 1324-5.

[10] "Pike, Strauss, Waymack, and Bacher were Republicans, while Lilienthal considered himself an independent" (Hewlett and Anderson, *op. cit.*, p. 622).

were being operated capably under contracts. The impairment and even stoppage of production that might have resulted from termination of these contracts and a shift to operations manned by Government employes, possibly without the benefit of the experienced private management engaged in the work, were risks too grave to be accepted. Since that time, upon several occasions, the Commission has studied the possibility of direct Government operation when undertaking new projects. In each case it has appeared that the project would be advanced most rapidly and efficiently by an experienced industrial concern. The unique capacity of American industry to develop new, better, and more economical ways of doing things is one of the greatest advantages that our Nation has in atomic energy development.[11]

3. From the outset, even in the days when fissionable material was most scarce, nuclear technology most secret, and civilian applications most uncertain, the explicit objective of the government was, in the words of the 1946 act, "strengthening free competition in private enterprise. . . ." Contracts with private industry —even the typical cost-plus-fixed-fee contracts under which industry risked little or nothing[12] but its reputation and some managerial talent—at least faced the Commission in the direction of its ultimate goal of establishing a viable, self-sustaining, self-financed, profit-making nuclear industry. (Whether it moved in that direction with due, or undue, deliberate speed is a matter about which opinions differ.)

4. Finally, contracting with outside groups had the double advantage of keeping these groups informed about highly classified activities that would otherwise be confined to narrower, official circles, and, in turn, bringing to the government a continuing flow of knowledge, ideas, and advice from a larger and more distinguished number of industrialists and scientists than would otherwise have participated in Commission affairs. In short, it helped to keep the AEC more alive and alert, administratively and technically.

Certain potential disadvantages of contract operation should be

[11] *AEC Contract Policy and Operations* (9th semi-annual report), Atomic Energy Commission (January 1951), pp. 39-40.

[12] From AEC accounts, one would say "nothing"; from industry, "little," since disallowances and costs not recognized by the government reduce the net value of the fee.

noted. "Labor management problems can be more acute in cost-type contractor operations; the timely flow of information between Government top management and the performers of the work may be more difficult; highly qualified contractors usually have their own organizational policies and practices which they prefer to follow and may resist some of the controls and procedural requirements which the Government deems necessary; valuable experience and technological advances may be initially in the hands of a few contractors. . . ."[13] The potential advantages of a good in-house laboratory should also be kept in mind. "These include more prompt responsiveness to agency needs, source of management personnel, greater technical participation in program and contractor evaluations and feasibility studies, and other actions requiring solid scientific and technical judgments. . . . an in-house laboratory, if it is strong scientifically, should be able to perform many of them equally well and perhaps better than most contractor-operated laboratories."[14]

Though AEC Chairman Glenn Seaborg was the source of both foregoing quotations, there is little evidence that the AEC has ever seriously considered the possibility of establishing, or converting one of their contractor-operated establishments into, a major inhouse facility.[15] And, in general, this seems to have been wise.

As the major operating principles of the Commission were determined or inherited in its formative days and continued thereafter with little change, there is little significant history to be written about them. Even the principal operating contractors long persisted with little change since the early postwar years. Accordingly, a functional rather than historical approach seems fruitful in examining AEC contract policies. (Some of the more

---

[13] From a statement of AEC Chairman Glenn Seaborg in *Systems Development and Management,* Hearings before a subcommittee of the House Government Operations Committee, 87 Cong. 2 sess. (1962), Pt. 5, p. 1645.

[14] *Ibid.,* p. 1646.

[15] When the National Reactor Testing Station was being set up in 1949-50, AEC staff investigated the experience of the Armed Services and the National Advisory Committee for Aeronautics with comparable test sites and the possibility of an inhouse operation was broached; but the Commissioners themselves apparently did not take the idea very seriously.

evolutionary, if not exactly historic, administrative changes are outlined in Chapter VI.) However, the departure of General Electric from the management of the Hanford laboratories in January 1965, its subsequent withdrawal from the management of other Hanford facilities, and planned changes in the contractual arrangements at Argonne and Idaho Falls announced in 1964 and 1965 marked the end of a contract era and the beginning of a new phase that we will shortly examine. Time will tell if this will be known as the phase of contractor "replacement" or "segmentation," "redirection" or "uncertainty," "invigoration" or "disappointment," but it has already posed significant and troublesome policy issues.

CHAPTER II

Choosing
Operating Contractors

Commission policy toward the contractors who operate its major plants and laboratories falls naturally into two phases that may be called the Old Order (the basic pattern of which was largely inherited from the Army), and the New (initiated in the early 1960's and still being defined).

The Old Order: A Chosen Few

One broad measure of the AEC domain (heartland and hinterland) is employment in the atomic energy field, estimated at 177,000 in January 1963, 120,500 of whom (including 7,000 AEC employees) were working in government-owned and 56,500 in private facilities (Table 1). All of the former and some of the latter received their salaries and wages, directly or (typically) indirectly, from government sources. Those working in government-owned facilities constitute the heart of the contract empire with which we will be concerned. Their number has peaked notably three times during (and troughed, following) three great periods of plant construction: at 130,000 in June 1944 (from which it ebbed to 41,500 in May 1947); about 70,000 during the 1948-49 phase of reconstruction and construction (dropping below 60,000 by the end of 1949); and 152,000 in August 1953, the high tide of the great 1951-54 program of plant expansion (from which it fell to

TABLE I

Persons in Atomic Energy Work, January 1963

Facilities	Thousands of persons
Government-owned facilities	120.5
Production and feed materials	47.5
Laboratory and research	44.5
Construction[a]	11.1
Federal service (including non-AEC)	8.2
Other	8.6
Private facilities	56.5
University (research, teaching, and support)	15.5
Not-for-profit laboratories	2.0
Profit-making	39.0
Reactor design, manufacture	10.1
Uranium mining, milling	7.4
Instrument and accelerator manufacture	6.0
Design and engineering of facilities	3.6
Other	11.9
Total	177.0

Source: Derived from *Annual Report to Congress of the Atomic Energy Commission for 1963* (January 1964), pp. 309-11.
[a] Includes a small percentage of construction of private facilities.

some 107,000 toward the end of 1955).[1] While capital expenditures and the employment of construction workers have fluctuated markedly, the steadier growth of operating and research and development budgets gradually increased employment in both government and private facilities. Counteracting these trends have been personnel reductions in the production plants due to process improvements; thus, employment at the Oak Ridge gaseous diffusion plants dropped from 11,000 in 1946 to 2,600 in January 1964. Program and production cuts have also led to periodic reductions in the contractor force: for example, 3,500 persons were dropped from contractor rolls in 1961 following cancellation of the aircraft nuclear propulsion work at facilities managed by

[1] For the June 1944 figure, see testimony by General Groves in *Military Establishment Appropriation Bill for 1947*, Hearings before a subcommittee of the House Appropriations Committee, 79 Cong. 2 sess. (1946), p. 920; subsequent trends are drawn from AEC semiannual and annual reports.

General Electric and Pratt & Whitney, and some 9,000 in 1965 as a result of cutbacks in the production of weapons and nuclear materials and changes in reactor development programs.[2]

AEC expenditures of $2.7 billion in fiscal year 1964 were distributed as follows:

Purpose	Millions of dollars
Procurement of raw materials	326
Production of nuclear materials	636
Weapons development and fabrication	805
Development of nuclear reactors	561
Other research and development	315
Administrative expenses	73
Other	22

This study will not consider the large but rapidly declining program of buying uranium ore on long-term fixed-price contracts; nor the large and also declining long-term fixed-price contracts for electric power (presumably included above under the cost of producing nuclear materials). It will focus instead upon the remaining contract programs, particularly those for the operation of government-owned facilities and for the conduct of research and development in both government and private laboratories (on which $1,505 million was expended in 1964, compared to $383 million ten years earlier).

The first noteworthy feature about these activities is how highly concentrated they have been, over half of both contract expenditures and contractor manpower, in recent years, having been in the hands of five industrial and two academic contractors: Union Carbide, General Electric, Bendix, Sandia,[3] Du Pont, and the Universities of California and Chicago. Table 2 lists the number of personnel and funds recently employed by these and other leading operating contractors in production, research and development, or service activities at AEC-owned facilities.

The degree of concentration is attributable mainly to technical factors: the enormous scale of plant required for the economic

[2] See *Annual Report to Congress of the Atomic Energy Commission for 1965*, pp. 44-45.

[3] A subsidiary of Western Electric, the Bell Telephone Laboratories, and the American Telephone & Telegraph Co.

TABLE 2

Contractor Costs and Employment at Major AEC Facilities, January 1964

(Dollar amounts in millions)

Contractor	Cost[a]	Personnel	Function	Location
Union Carbide	$ 275.7	14,072	P, R	Oak Ridge, Paducah
General Electric	177.8	12,765	P, R	Hanford, Evendale, Schenectady, Pinellas
U. of California	212.8	12,559	R	Berkeley, Livermore, Los Alamos, Las Vegas
Bendix	101.1	8,173	P	Kansas City
Sandia	148.7	8,108	P, R	Albuquerque, Livermore
Du Pont	85.0	6,321	P, R	Savannah River
U. of Chicago	48.7	5,203	R	Argonne, Idaho Falls
Above 7 contractors	$1,049.8	67,201		
Reynolds Electric	69.1	4,718	S	Las Vegas
Mason & Hanger	26.4	4,069	P	Clarksville, Burlington, Amarillo, San Antonio
Westinghouse	52.6	3,691	R	Pittsburgh
Atomic International	63.6	3,638	R	Canoga Park
Dow Chemical	28.3	3,110	P	Rocky Flats
Associated Universities	36.1	3,030	R	Brookhaven
ACF Industries	36.2	2,695	P	Albuquerque, Las Vegas
Edgerton, Germeshausen & Grier	11.8	2,392	R	Boston, Las Vegas, Santa Barbara
Phillips Petroleum	16.2	2,118	R, S	Idaho Falls
National Lead	26.0	2,054	P	Fernald
Next 10 contractors	$ 366.3	31,515		
Total, above 17 contractors	$1,416.1	98,716		

a Fiscal year 1963 operating costs.
P—production of weapons or nuclear materials
R—research or development
S—service

14

production of a large volume of nuclear materials; the exceptional requirements of electric power, water, security, reliability, and safety, which have served to concentrate production, development, and testing at a few locations; and the small incremental cost of conducting additional work at existing facilities where large investments have already been made (of the $7.7 billion invested by the AEC in plant and equipment through fiscal year 1963, $5.4 billion had been put into facilities managed by the seven contractors enumerated above).

However, there can be little doubt that other factors have also operated: the administrative economies and convenience of dealing with a small number of prime contractors; the advantages which special knowledge and experience have given contractors long associated with nuclear programs; the Commission's reliance on these contractors; and the contractors' influence, most effective where it has been unsought. The agency could not have functioned with so small a staff had it not delegated great responsibilities to a few contractors (many smaller contractors would have required a larger staff for purposes of control and coordination); and the perpetuation of a few, trusted and (for the most part) responsive contractors enabled the government to get its work done and yet maintain that tight control needed in top secret operations.

The concentration of prime contracts does not mean that AEC money has gone to only a few contractors. A number of programs have dispersed relatively small sums widely—for example, the program of small lump sum contracts for scientific research by university faculty. Subcontracting, and construction and procurement contracts have also spread AEC funds to a broad spectrum of industry: in fiscal year 1963, for example, the Sandia Corporation alone had some 6,000 industrial and commercial suppliers across the land; and the Bendix Corporation, 2,500. In fiscal year 1962, when AEC prime contracts totaled $2.7 billion, $.7 billion was subcontracted, mainly for materials, supplies, and equipment. However, in the areas of our special interest, research and development and managerial services, there was relatively little subcontracting (Table 3).

The other notable feature of the big AEC operating contracts

TABLE 3

Volume of AEC Prime Contracts and Subcontracts, by Purpose, Fiscal Year 1962

(in millions of dollars)

Purpose	Prime contracts	Subcontracts
a. Managerial and other services	$1,094	$ 47
b. Research and development	692	24
c. Material, supplies, and equipment	576	612
d. Rent and utilities	212	14
e. Construction	128	35
f. Architect-engineer	35	4
Total	$2,737	$736

Source: Small Business Administration. The principal components of line *a*, evidently, are contracts for the management of plants producing fissionable materials; of line *c*, contracts for the purchase of uranium ore. As line *b* reports only $692 million expenditures for R&D in 1962 compared to the $1,284 million reported by the National Science Foundation, it is probable that line *a* includes a large volume of R&D (see *Federal Funds for Research, Development, and Other Scientific Activities, Fiscal Years 1962, 1963, and 1964*, Volume XII, National Science Foundation, 1964, p. 111).

has been their continuity. Until 1965, few changes were made in the contractors managing major installations and these, confined mainly to the 1946-49 transition from military to civilian direction and from wartime to peacetime conditions, were generally initiated by the contractor rather than the Commission.[4] Du Pont, which had undertaken the management of Hanford only for the duration of the war, insisted on leaving thereafter; similarly, the University of Chicago and Tennessee-Eastman asked to be relieved of their responsibilities at Oak Ridge, and the University of California, of its growing ordnance responsibilities at Sandia.

The broad statement that a contractor "asked to be relieved" does not always exhaust the subtleties of the situation, since there are ways by which the government can lead a contractor to make

[4] Cf. the May 1962 statement of Commission Chairman Glenn Seaborg: ". . . our experience has been mostly limited to changes where on-the-job contractors wanted to leave, or where, for other reasons, there has been mutual agreement to change contractors. We have not attempted to change an otherwise satisfactory contractor for the purpose of broadening participation in the operation of AEC production facilities. . . ." Things were soon to change! *AEC Authorizing Legislation Fiscal Year 1963*, Hearings before the . . . Joint Committee on Atomic Energy, 87 Cong. 2 sess. (1962), p. 405.

or withhold such a request. Thus, General James McCormack, director of the AEC Division of Military Applications, stated in July 1949 that ". . . some six months ago, the University of California asked to be relieved of the operation of the Sandia Laboratory." However, the Commission Chairman David Lilienthal has put a slightly different complexion on the change: ". . . when a new bomb establishment was to be set up near Los Alamos, instead of asking the University of California to add this to its Los Alamos contract, I persuaded the Bell Telephone System to take this contractual responsibility. . . ."[5] At any rate, the Du Pont departure seems clear, since Secretary of War Robert Patterson made a strong plea to the company to remain, which it politely declined.[6]

With three exceptions, there were no further changes of note until 1964. The exceptions involved consolidations at Oak Ridge in 1947 and 1948, at the Nevada Test Site in 1952, and at the National Reactor Testing Station in Idaho in 1953, each of which led to the replacement of one or more contractors. (A few contractors have had programs terminated—e.g., the Dana heavy water plant managed by Du Pont and the aircraft nuclear propulsion work of General Electric and Pratt & Whitney; certain service contractors were dropped and the responsibilities of others curtailed when the government-owned towns of Oak Ridge and Richland became self-governing.) The vintage of principal operating and service contracts is indicated in Table 4.

The New Order: Contractor Change and Segmentation

This long idyll between the Commission and its operating contractors was disturbed in 1963. New criteria announced in May 1963 provided that service-type contractors at AEC installations were normally to be replaced by the solicitation of proposals "at the extension of the current contract term unless the Commission

---

[5] See *Investigations into the United States Atomic Energy Project*, Joint Committee on Atomic Energy, 81 Cong. 1 sess. (1949), Pt. 20, pp. 803, 827; and David Lilienthal, *Change, Hope, and the Bomb* (Princeton University Press, 1963), p. 79.

[6] See Hewlett and Anderson, *The New World, 1939/1946* (Pennsylvania State University Press, University Park, 1962), p. 629.

TABLE 4

Inception of Major AEC Contracts[a]

Initial Contract	Contractor	Location
Jan. 1943	University of California	Los Alamos, N. Mex.
Jan. 1943	Union Carbide Nuclear Co.	Oak Ridge, Tenn.
May 1943	University of California	Berkeley, Calif.
Apr. 1946	University of Chicago	Argonne, Ill.
May 1946	General Electric Co.	Richland, Wash.; Schenectady, N. Y.
Jan. 1947	Associated Universities, Inc.	Brookhaven, L. I., N. Y.
Aug. 1947	Mason & Hanger[b]	Burlington, Iowa
Jan. 1948	Monsanto Research Corp.	Miamisburg, Ohio
May 1948	Atomics International Division, North American Aviation, Inc.	Santa Susanna, Calif.; Canoga Park, Calif.
Nov. 1948	Bendix Corp.	Kansas City, Mo.
Dec. 1948	Westinghouse Electric Corp.	Pittsburgh, Pa.
July 1949	Sandia Corp.	Albuquerque, N. Mex.
Aug. 1950	E. I. duPont de Nemours & Co.	Savannah River, S. C.
Nov. 1950	Phillips Petroleum Co.	Idaho Falls, Idaho
Jan. 1951	Dow Chemical Co.	Rocky Flats, Colo.
May 1951	National Lead Co.	Fernald, Ohio
July 1951	Edgerton, Germeshausen & Grier, Inc.	Las Vegas, Nev.
Oct. 1951	Holmes & Narver, Inc.	Las Vegas, Nev.
Sept. 1952	ACF Industries, Inc.	Albuquerque, N. Mex.
Oct. 1952	Goodyear Atomic Corp.	Portsmouth, Ohio
Dec. 1952	Reynolds Electrical and Engineering Co., Inc.	Las Vegas, Nev.

Source: Atomic Energy Commission

[a] Operating or service contracts more than ten years old (in June 1964), with operating costs of over $10 million in fiscal year 1963. The "initial date" of the first five entries refers to Manhattan Project contracts. In some cases, such as the work of the University of California at Berkeley, even earlier dates might be given by citing contracts issued by the Office of Scientific Research and Development (see also Table 9). These contracts have not, of course, remained untouched since the initial date; they have been periodically renegotiated and extended usually for five or three years at a time.

[b] Operated under an Army contract until October 1963.

determines that replacement of the existing contractor would be greatly adverse to the best interests of the Government." In the case of operating or managerial contracts, proposals were to be solicited:

1. Where the existing operating contractor's performance is considered not better than average; or,

2. When the circumstances underscore the high desirability of giving

adequate opportunity to other organizations to compete for the business of supplying services to the Commission.

The first criterion was little more stringent than the standing criterion of "marginal performance," and the second was notable chiefly for its vagueness, although one of the "circumstances" the Commission had in mind was suggested by the further information that, in the selection process, "some weight" would be given "to firms that have made a substantial investment in the commercial atomic energy industry or have demonstrated concrete interest in participating in private commercial atomic energy activities."[7]

That firms operating government facilities on cost-plus-fixed-fee (CPFF) contracts had gained thereby (if they wished) an advantage in the commercial nuclear industry was clear. The advantage stemmed from personal acquaintanceships, special and often classified technical information, knowledge of AEC program needs, and, most valuable and least communicable of all, the experience acquired by staff subsequently transferred to the contractor's private nuclear business:

If one examines the large reactor manufacturing companies that are today quoting fixed prices on nuclear power plants, you will find that in almost all cases the key people in these commercial organizations received much of their training and experience under operating contracts for the Atomic Energy Commission, or in the Commission, and subsequently transferred into the commercial divisions of their companies as peaceful applications developed.[8]

Admiral Hyman Rickover has further observed that:

A company may spend, say 1 or 2 percent of its gross income on its own research and development work; but when they do Government research and development they thereby get large additional sums of money to do such work. In this way they enhance their competitive position without having to use their own money. . . . In essence Government-financed research and development subsidizes and augments their

[7] "New AEC Criteria Apply to Replacement of Operating and Service-Type Contractors," AEC press release, May 24, 1963.

[8] Ernest Tremmel, Director of the AEC Division of Industrial Participation, in *Proceedings of R&D Symposium. The Impact of Government Research and Development Expenditures on Industrial Growth*, March 13-14, 1963, National Security Industrial Association, Washington, D. C., p. 142.

own research and development effort, and so enhances their competitive position.[9]

The AEC and its operating contractors have gone to every reasonable and some exceptional lengths to avoid conflicts between a contractor's responsibilities to the government and his private commercial interests, and to ensure that the latter were not unfairly aided or subsidized by the former. For example, purchases of a contractor's commercial products usually have been handled by the AEC field office rather than the contractor; the office has been kept informed about meetings between staff of a contractor's home office and the government installation; the AEC owns all patents, drawings, and technical information produced with its money and has made these available to all; subject only to security clearances, rival firms have been given access to government facilities managed by private contractors and have often received unique training there (Goodyear employees operating the Portsmouth diffusion plant were trained by Union Carbide employees at Oak Ridge, and Westinghouse staff have learned what they could at the Hanford and Knolls works managed by General Electric); transfers of staff to a contractor's private business have been undertaken with the knowledge and usually, but not necessarily, the approval of the AEC. Nevertheless, there can be little doubt that some firms have obtained from their government contracts a commercial advantage in their private nuclear business. It is no coincidence that the two monarchs of the civilian nuclear power business, Westinghouse and General Electric, have long operated major AEC reactor laboratories.[10] But the advantage

---

[9] *Patent Policies of Government Departments and Agencies—1960,* Conference of Subcommitte on Monopoly of Senate Select Committee on Small Business and Vice Admiral H. G. Rickover, 86 Cong. 2 sess. (1960), p. 3.

[10] Cf. the following entry for November 26, 1946 in the diary of the AEC's first chairman: "We [the new Commission] spent most time on a contract with General Electric for the operation of Hanford *and* the operation of an expensive laboratory at Schenectady which the contract provides that the Government will pay for. When I first heard of this, I didn't like it; didn't like it at all. . . . And the more we looked at it, the less we liked the deal. . . . the Schenectady laboratory was provided [by General Groves] as a means of inducing General Electric to operate Hanford, though the two are not otherwise related. And the company could stop the operation of Hanford almost whenever it chose, and still have the laboratory." *The Journals of David E. Lilienthal,* Vol. II, *The Atomic Energy Years 1945-1950* (Harper, 1964), p. 113.

The point about Groves was disputed by a qualified commentator who denied that

they have thereby gained should not be exaggerated. G.E. and Westinghouse are preeminent in non-nuclear as well as nuclear power, and their position in both fields derives from their financial strength, familiarity with the needs of electric utilities, and ability to stand behind their products to the utilities' satisfaction.

As long as the nuclear industry was entirely owned by the government and confined predominantly to military objectives, with small prospect of a free market developing for privately manufactured nuclear products, there was little pressure or incentive to disrupt the existing management of AEC installations; and as long as the production of nuclear materials and weapons proceeded at high levels, a possible slowdown due to changing contractors could not be contemplated. The gradual growth of a private nuclear industry following the Atomic Energy Act of 1954 and the perceptible abatement of (or, at least, the perceptible effort to abate) the nuclear arms race accompanying the 1958-61 nuclear test moratorium, and the 1963 treaty banning atmospheric tests, altered both conditions and facilitated pressure from industry for a piece of the large AEC pie held by operating contractors. A letter from Richard Bokum, president of the United Nuclear Corporation, to AEC General Manager Luedecke in August 1962 put the matter forcefully:

An important factor affecting the growth of companies and competitive position in the nuclear industry is whether or not they are participating in the Atomic Energy Commission program as operators of AEC-owned facilities under cost-plus-fixed-fee contracts. The companies which have participated have been able to train personnel in atomic technology. . . . Moreover, they have been able to operate largely without risk. All this gives them a preferred competitive position as well as unique financial and organizational stability.

---

the laboratory contract had been given as a "sweetener," or for any other reason than the active furtherance of the nuclear program. For his part, Harry Winne, General Electric vice president, has stated that "our main reason for going into this project [the management of Hanford and Knolls] at all is that here is a development of atomic energy which has at least the possibility of being a factor in making electric power more readily available, available over greater areas and possibly at lower costs, for the future than it is now.

"Any development of that nature is of interest in the General Electric Co., because we are an electrical-manufacturing company; and the more readily electric power is available to everybody, the more chance we have to sell our products." *Investigation into the United States Atomic Energy Project,* Hearings before the Joint Committee on Atomic Energy, 81 Cong. 1 sess. (1949), Pt. 14, p. 602.

. . . As far as we can tell, only 4 of the 22 . . . [major AEC operating] contractors . . . have made significant private investments in the development of a free competitive nuclear industry . . . the Commission has a right to expect companies working on its operating contracts . . . to reinvest some portion of their profits and apply their experience in a program designed to enable AEC . . . to establish a competitive private nuclear industry.

We are prepared to do that. . . . I would very much like to discuss with you . . . the possibility of United Nuclear Corp. being given the chance to make a proposal to operate an appropriate Atomic Energy Commission facility.[11]

The inconsistency of the two arguments—operating contractors have a commercial advantage, but only four of twenty-two employed it—may be noted. Essentially, this outsider trying to break into the circle of operating contractors was saying: replace those operating contractors with a substantial private nuclear business because they receive a competitive advantage, and replace the others because they are *not* taking advantage of their position. The evident logical, if not political, anomaly of promoting private enterprise by various forms of government subsidy may also be noted.

In October 1961, the Commission approved the establishment of a policy for the selective replacement of existing operating or service contractors and the segmentation of certain major facilities, but little more was then done about it. Prodded at hearings by the Joint Committee on Atomic Energy in April and May, by the House Government Operations Committee in August,[12] and

[11] *Development, Growth, and State of the Atomic Energy Industry,* Hearings before the Joint Committee on Atomic Energy, 88 Cong. 1 sess. (1963), Pt. 2, pp. 945-6. Mr. Bokum proposed only that some of a company's *profits* be reinvested, one reader observed. "I doubt if profits to industries from AEC contractors—even if all were reinvested—would build a very large nuclear industry." "Why should the Commission have a right to expect them [contractors] to reinvest a portion of their profits?" asked another.

[12] The following exchange took place at a Joint Committee hearing in April 1962:
Senator Pastore [vice chairman]: "What is the Commission's policy for the award and renewal of operating contracts at Commission facilities?"
General Betts [Director, Division of Military Application]: ". . . one would have to have some fairly good reason for wanting to get rid of the old contractor for a change to look attractive, because of the know-how that has been built up within a going concern. Consequently, it is very rare that we find it necessary to change contractors, or advisable. . . ."

again by newly appointed Commissioner James Ramey (an alumnus of the Joint Committee staff) in an address before the Atomic Industrial Forum in November 1962,[13] the Commission finally responded with the aforenoted May 1963 announcement (incorporated in procurement regulations in December 1963).

It was perhaps and perhaps not coincidental that in January 1964 the AEC and the General Electric Company jointly announced that the Hanford contract which G.E. had held since 1946 would be segmented and transferred to a number of other contractors in an effort to widen industrial participation and stimulate economic diversification in the Richland area. The subsequent letter of intent given to the nonprofit[14] Battelle Memorial

---

Mr. Ramey [staff director]: "I think on your weapons contractors and your production to a lesser extent that it is quite understandable. . . . In your development contracts . . . the other contractors are getting hungry. . . . On major operating contractors for, say Oak Ridge or Argonne, or at Idaho and so on, on your peacetime business, it does seem that you ought to look and see whether or not you should not get proposals from other outfits." *AEC Authorizing Legislation Fiscal Year 1963*, Hearings before the Subcommittee on Legislation of the Joint Committee on Atomic Energy, 87 Cong. 2 sess. (1962), pp. 41-2; see also pp. 403-12.

During the August hearings of the Government Operations Committee subcommittee chaired by Chet Holifield, then also chairman of the Joint Committee on Atomic Energy, the following exchange took place:

Mr. Roback [staff administrator]: "The contractors who came in gained experience and were efficient; they acquired the technology and became more and more efficient, and there was a rationale for continuing them.

"On the other hand, the rationale which brought them in the first place, namely, that there would be a transition to industry, isn't being met because you are not rotating contractors and broadening the industrial base."

Mr. Seaborg [AEC Chairman]: "There is, in a sense, a bit of basic conflict there, yes, sir."

Mr. Roback: "Has any consideration been given, or would it be disruptive of an efficient program, to have rotation of AEC industry contractors?"

Mr. Seaborg: "We have been giving more consideration to this recently." *Systems Development and Management*, Hearings Before a Subcommittee on Government Operations, House of Representatives. 87 Cong. 2 sess. (1962), Pt. 5, p. 1662.

[13] In the course of this address, Ramey remarked that ". . . in my opinion, in connection with the renewal of operating contracts the Commission should seriously consider some means of taking into account the experience and interest in continued industrial development of outside industrial organizations." *Atom Forum 1962, Proceedings of the 1962 Annual Conference of the Atomic Industrial Forum*, Atomic Industrial Forum (New York, 1963), p. 128.

[14] The usage "not-for-profit" is preferred by some for "nonprofit" but fee-taking research institutes such as Battelle, particularly those which undertake applied and proprietary work.

Institute in July 1964 for management of the Hanford laboratory thus became the first concrete manifestation of the new AEC policy on operating contractors.[15]

Sharing with Westinghouse a virtual duopoly of the nuclear reactor industry, General Electric was an obvious target for a Commission instructed by statute to forestall the growth of monopoly in this industry.[16] But the Hanford change was not so much a consequence of such general policy considerations as of a concrete economic crisis that, long foreseen, was precipitated in January 1964 when President Johnson announced that four plutonium-producing reactors, including three of the nine at Hanford, would be shut down. Some 2,000 jobs of the 8,300 in the one-industry Richland area would be affected. For its part, G.E. was not unhappy to relinquish the Hanford contract since potential conflicts of interest had begun increasingly to embarrass the free development, and private patentability, of its commercial reactor operations.

The AEC had a special sense of obligation to Richland residents, for it had owned the town, built originally by the Manhattan District, and only in 1957 were residents permitted to buy

[15] In conformance with the new policy on service contracts, H. K. Ferguson, a service contractor at the Idaho Falls National Reactor Testing Station, had been replaced some months earlier at the expiration of a contract term that had begun in 1958.

[16] Cf. the following discussion between Richard Bokum, president of the United Nuclear Corp., and Congressmen Chet Holifield and Craig Hosmer.

Bokum: "To me the future of this [civilian nuclear] business is in the power generation and this is why we vertically integrated. If we hadn't vertically integrated and we became strictly an ore supplier, we would be then at the mercy of the people that were buying our uranium. If it became a monopoly as it is today we would be at the mercy of two companies . . . because they are going to dictate the price that they are going to pay us."

Holifield: "Who?"

Bokum: "Westinghouse and General Electric."

Holifield: "In the first place, I do not think they are going to have a monopoly in the reactor business if this committee has anything to do with it. We are going to support other types of reactors, I hope, which will give them some competition. . . ."

Bokum: ". . . General Electric and Westinghouse have been given most of the R&D work, the CPFF dollar that the Government spends. They are both operators of big Government facilities. They have this competitive advantage. . . ."

Hosmer: "Let us admit that it is a bad deal and it ought to be broken up." *Private Ownership of Special Nuclear Materials*, Hearings before the Subcommittee on Legislation of the Joint Committee on Atomic Energy, 88 Cong. 1 sess. (1963), p. 127.

their homes. Despite its isolation, Richland had potential industrial advantages including transportation facilities and abundant power and water. Accordingly, local citizens and the AEC embarked on a campaign to attract enough private and government work to replace that which would be withdrawn. By segmenting the Hanford operation and leasing or selling various portions, it was hoped to stimulate private investment and thereby create additional employment. Private business activity that would not be tolerated (on grounds of conflict of interest, if not monopoly) if conducted by General Electric while holding a contract for the entire Hanford operation, might be acceptable if undertaken by another—particularly a nonprofit—organization.

Thus, the Battelle Memorial Institute, the new contractor for the Hanford laboratories, has been encouraged to "seek an expanded scope of work from private organizations and other Government agencies as well as carrying on contract work for the AEC."[17] Battelle's readiness to invest a large amount of its own funds as well as the entire contract fee in a major diversification program at the laboratory (whose broader horizon is now symbolized by its new name, the Pacific Northwest Laboratory) were important factors in its receiving the contract award. It was proposed to grant another contractor, Computer Services Corp., a permit to use an IBM 7090 computer, and then to contract for AEC services on this machine. Although the fulfillment of these services would be the contractor's primary responsibility, he

. . . will be expected to exert maximum effort in establishing with private capital a regional computer center in Richland from which private work can be performed in addition to the AEC work. To further encourage the development of private work, AEC will permit the selected contractor to use its existing facilities and equipment in performance of private work. . . .[18]

The remainder of the installation was to be segmented into four parts, the operation of which had, by the end of 1965, been allotted to other contractors: the plutonium reactors and fuel prepara-

[17] AEC press release, January 21, 1964.
[18] "Request for Comment and Expression of Interest-Automatic Data Processing Service—Request for Proposal," U. S. Atomic Energy Commission, Richland Operations Office, May 28, 1964.

tion works to Douglas United Nuclear, a joint venture of Douglas Aircraft and United Nuclear Corp.; the chemical separation facilities to Isochem, a joint venture of U. S. Rubber and Martin-Marietta; transportation, utilities, warehousing, and other services to ITT Federal Support Services, a subsidiary of International Telephone and Telegraph Corp.; and radiation protection services to the United States Testing Co. Altogether, the six new contractors had pledged to invest some $36.5 million in private activities that were expected to employ 1,110 persons by 1970.[19]

Patently, the Commission has embarked on an experiment, the encouragement of private work on government land and/or in government facilities, with profound implications for public policy. The good intentions of AEC staff and Richland citizens were clear, and the successful adjustment not only of this community, but of others from a predominantly military to a more balanced civilian economy, was surely a desirable national objective. Nevertheless, the wisdom of the particular contractual policy employed may be questioned, since it is difficult to establish a policy for, or confine it to, a single site, and the widespread adoption of this policy by the government could pose problems greater than those it was designed to deal with. Even from the standpoint of the AEC alone, the problems of Richland were but a foretaste of what may subsequently be faced by other sites like Los Alamos, Oak Ridge, and Savannah River, whose economic fortunes, to a greater or lesser degree, have been tied to the scale of nuclear, and especially nuclear weapons, expenditures. The uncomfortable position of the AEC was evidenced not only by cries of "unfair competition" and "government subsidy" voiced by some companies, but by its request for legislation to authorize the sale of property at Hanford that was *not* surplus to AEC or government needs, in order to eliminate the most awkward posture of encouraging private enterprise in a government installation.[20] The ad hoc legisla-

[19] See *Annual Report to Congress of the Atomic Energy Commission for 1965* (January 1966), pp. 26-29.
[20] S. 2816 introduced by Senator Pastore on May 7, 1964, would authorize the Commission "for a period of not more than five years . . . to sell . . . lease . . . and otherwise dispose of real property . . . and . . . equipment . . . in and near Richland, Washington, upon a determination by the Commission that such disposition will serve to prevent or reduce adverse economic impact of actual or anticipated reductions in Com-

tive and contract policies pursued at Hanford were an enterprising but insufficient substitute for an adequate national program to deal with an important national problem.

The breakup of the Hanford contract, the prospective segmentation of the National Reactor Testing Station operation announced in February 1965, and bruited changes at other major installations generated a good deal of anxiety and uncertainty among AEC and contractor staff, which might have been reduced by clarifying the scope and applicability of the Commission's new operating contract policies. Such clarification was, however, slow in coming—partly because AEC staff were divided about the new policy, and partly because of its inherent complexities and uncertainties.

The number of operating contracts renewed or extended between 1962 and 1964, for at least some of which competitive proposals might have been requested, convinced close observers that the staff were not all ardently devoted to contractor change and still less to segmentation. One old-time AEC hand freely volunteered, "I think they're getting into the biggest mess there ever was out at Hanford," and others agreed. A change of contractor, it was pointed out, necessitates an overlap of several months in the senior personnel of outgoing and incoming contractors, at dou-

mission programs in that area and thereby contribute to the retention and recruitment of personnel essential to continuing Commission programs . . . . disposition shall be made on such terms as the Commission determines will provide reasonable compensation . . . considering the current fair market value . . . and the benefits to the Government from such disposition." AEC General Manager Luedecke explained that the requested bill "permits the Commission to dispose of such property at less than its fair market value, if the Commission determines that such disposal is in the best interest of accomplishing AEC's program activities. It should be emphasized that disposals under this authority are of property which is not excess to the needs of AEC or surplus to the overall needs of the Government." The Commission could, furthermore, "dispose of property for purposes unrelated to atomic energy. . . ." The measure became law in August 1964, with modifications which removed the five year limitation and the references to essential personnel and to benefits to the Government; the act also added a political safeguard that, prior to the disposition of any property, "the basis for the proposed disposition (with necessary background and explanatory data) shall be submitted to the Joint Committee on Atomic Energy, and a period of forty-five days shall elapse. . . ." See *AEC Omnibus Bills for 1963 and 1964,* Hearings before the Subcommittee on Legislation of the Joint Committee on Atomic Energy, 88 Cong. 2 sess. (1964), pp. 130, 167, and 259; and Public Law 88-394, 88 Cong., S. 2963 (Aug. 1, 1964), Sec. 4.

bled expense, and a protracted period of accommodation between Commission and contractor staff. Examples were related of the difficulties experienced in the early years of major contracts that were ironed out as government and private staffs gradually learned to work with each other. And, indeed, a visitor to some (not all) long established AEC installations was impressed with the smoothness and closeness of relations between the two staffs, and the virtual identity of their interests and outlook.

But what kind of effort can be expected of a contractor who has no expectation of renewal? After the introductory period of adjustment, which may last a year or more, a short productive period may follow; then, will there not be some loss of interest a year or eighteen months before the contract terminates, as the thoughts of key people turn elsewhere and the AEC contemplates another round of proposals? One commentator reported a letdown "all along the line" and "an aura of uneasiness . . . difficult to combat," at an AEC facility awaiting the designation of a new contractor.[21]

If these critics questioned the wisdom of changing contractors, segmentation they condemned outright. At Oak Ridge, Las Vegas, and Idaho Falls, a decade or more ago, the AEC moved in the opposite direction, consolidating previously segmented operations in the interests of efficiency. "The Commission will look kind of ridiculous when it starts to reexamine the ——— contract," one official declared. "Total replacement instead of segmentation would have been cleaner, more manageable and would certainly cost the taxpayers less money," another suggested. Different contractors on the same site lead, it was said, to different standards and practice; to duplication of services; to different wage scales, vacation terms, and personnel benefits; frequently, to different unions, with a consequent jockeying for advantage and unsettled labor relations; to larger total fees, since the AEC fee curve is reduced proportionately as the size of the contract rises; to an enlarged AEC staff; and, in toto, to greater expense. "I see very little benefits and a whole lot of costs [in this] . . . spreading the work,"

[21] He added, "The inordinately long time the Commission claims to require to select a replacement contractor . . . does not aid in maintaining an energetic and dedicated work force."

remarked an AEC officer, with over twenty years experience in the nuclear enterprise, who hoped that President Johnson's cost reduction campaign would restrict segmentation to a few sites. ". . . the General Electric Company had the strength to hold the Hanford operation together. It remains to be seen whether the Hanford Operations Office can do it," an industrial executive remarked.

For its part, the AEC was aware of the problems segmentation might pose, but felt that these could be reduced by vigilant contract negotiation and administration, and, insofar as they could not, were simply a price that had to be paid to achieve important objectives. All operating contracts required AEC approval of wage and salary policies, and a uniform structure was maintained in the three new contracts negotiated at Hanford up to November 1965. Total fees in the segmented operation would be higher, but, if the volume of private work rose, the contractor's overhead chargeable to the AEC would decrease. Nor was it insignificant that two of the more important Hanford contractors were joint venture corporations, each formed by the union of two independent companies, an arrangement that facilitates the establishment of contract terms and personnel practices compatible with the local scene (and the local AEC) rather than with each company's private policies.[22]

The inherent complexities of the new policy stemmed from the fact that it was not so much one policy as three policies rolled into one, whose net outcome could not readily be predicted at any site. There were the objectives 1. of diversifying the economy and, thereby, enhancing the viability of communities endangered by budgetary cutbacks; 2. of rewarding companies investing in the nuclear industry; and 3. of promoting competition by strengthening lesser companies already in the nuclear industry and inducing new companies to enter the industry.

The inconvenience and expense of contractor change could be

---

[22] ". . . a joint venture corporation is reasonably free to do the Commission's bidding in areas such as labor policy, wage rates, salary structure, employee benefits, etcetera," one industry spokesman declared. "These will bear no necessary relationship to the personnel policies of the parent corporations.

"The practical result . . . is to create corporate entities that, in effect, are captive to the Commission even though they are not government-owned."

discounted as a price it was necessary to pay for introducing a greater degree of vitality and a broader range of participation into nuclear industry and science. But two serious reservations must still be voiced about the Commission's new policy (or policies). By seeking to accomplish too much with limited resources, the AEC may accomplish less than if it concentrated upon fewer objectives. (Thus, the administrative problems—and costs—of contractor change would be reduced, while the fee would be increased and thereby rendered more effective in shoring up competition, if Hanford had been broken into fewer pieces.) And its method of encouraging private investment in the nuclear industry poses a decided danger of conflict of interest. The original choice of the Phillips Petroleum Company to operate the National Reactor Testing Station had been made, in part, because the company did *not* have a private investment in the reactor business and hence could administer tests fairly and report results fully, without fear of favoritism or suspicion of putting its own interests before those of a competitor or the government. Under the new policy of giving preference to firms with a substantial private nuclear investment, the Commission was dispensing with a contractor like Phillips for precisely that virtue for which it had previously contracted.[23] Conflict of interest is a problem of ethics, not of corporate size; and as operating contractors with a financial interest in the nuclear industry proliferate, and the standards to which some are subject are liberalized, this problem is likely to be aggravated. Apparently, the AEC shares this expectation, to judge from its markedly ambivalent statement that "Conflicts of interests between commercial and contract activities [offer grounds for replacing an operating contractor] when found to outweigh the advantages of using contractors who are demonstrating a sufficient interest in the field of atomic energy to have maintained their

[23] The Commission proposed to retain Phillips for the reactor safety program at NRTS but to transfer operation of three test reactors, the chemical processing plant, and local services to another contractor. Chairman Seaborg made it clear that Phillips had an "excellent record of accomplishment" and that the decision to segment its contract was "in no sense a reflection on the past performance of Phillips." "AEC to Offer Other Organizations Opportunity to Perform Contract Work at NRTS," AEC press release (Feb. 5, 1965).

own commercial program and thus are assisting in establishing a private, competitive nuclear industry. . . ."[24] That "when found to outweigh" is a pit into which the best intentioned men may fall.

Selection of Operating Contractors

AEC procurement regulations provide an admirable set of criteria and procedures to guide selection boards in preparing a list of firms invited to submit contract proposals and in evaluating the proposals received. The purpose of these procedures is to "Insure consistent treatment of firms under consideration" and to select "the best contractor for a given job"; AEC policy, it is stated, is "to consider as many firms, within practical limits, as may be well-qualified to perform the desired work."[25]

The only thing seriously wrong with these procedures is that they have not really been employed in the selection of certain critical operating contractors. Elaborate selection procedures do not seem to have been used at all for this purpose in the days of the Manhattan District or the Office of Scientific Research and Development. The extraordinary pressures for secrecy, speed, and technical reliability; the scarcity of persons (let alone firms) capable of nuclear work; and the great wartime delegations of authority resulted in many of the key decisions (which the AEC and the nation inherited) being made by very few people and on relatively little hard evidence of the kind that would withstand scrutiny by a congressional committee.

The historical record suggests that the personal experience and judgment of one or two men were often critical in the selection process. Thus, Arthur Compton relates how, though "the main focus of these activities at this time [early 1942] was in Columbia and Princeton" he resolved to centralize work on "the plutonium project" at his own institution, Chicago. Thereupon, Fermi, Szilard, and Herbert Anderson moved to Chicago from Columbia; Eugene Wigner, John Wheeler, and Edward Creutz moved from Princeton; and Glenn Seaborg, Frank Spedding, Norman Hilber-

---

[24] *Federal Register*, Sept. 24, 1964, p. 13254.
[25] *Federal Register*, Dec. 28, 1963, p. 14427.

ry, Martin Whitaker, H. A. Potratz, and others from other institutions.[26] Had Compton resolved on Columbia or Princeton, for which he had ample grounds, it seems likely that the Argonne National Laboratory would not have been located near, or been managed by, the University of Chicago; and the Brookhaven National Laboratory, established in 1946 to satisfy the scientists of the Northeast, might never have been born (or might have been lodged, instead, in the Midwest).

Similarly, the fact that Conant and Groves esteemed Du Pont highly, the former having been a Du Pont consultant and the latter having worked closely with the company on Army construction programs, played an important part in their decision to bring Du Pont into the plutonium work at Hanford (and, subsequently, in the return of Du Pont to operate the plutonium reactors at Savannah River). "After I had studied all the possibilities," Groves has recalled, "I concluded that only one firm was capable of handling . . . the job. That firm was Du Pont."[27] However, Compton, who as Groves notes had been a Westinghouse engineer for three years and a General Electric consultant for seventeen, proposed at one stage to call in the latter two firms and to place less reliance on Du Pont—and, of course, both firms later demonstrated their capacity in the nuclear field.[28]

The point is not that the decisions to contract with Chicago and Du Pont were unwise or unwarranted; both decisions were clearly warranted and both passed a critical, if crude, test: they succeeded. But they were determined more by the rapid judgment of a few men in key places than by a protracted, methodical process of examining and evaluating possible alternatives. As one reader familiar with Manhattan Project contractor selections put it:

We did *not* prepare elaborate studies—you're dead right. But there was nobody in the country who knew the management of these chemical companies as well as [Groves] . . .—the tremendous superiority of duPont. . . . We didn't take all year to do it, and write elaborate docu-

[26] Arthur Compton, *Atomic Quest* (Oxford University Press, New York, 1956), pp. 80-83, 93.

[27] Leslie R. Groves, *Now It Can Be Told* (Harper & Brothers, New York, 1962), p. 42.

[28] *Ibid.*, p. 56.

ments. It was done very carefully and there was always a definite reason for doing it—it wasn't a haphazard affair. . . . [We] always [got] . . . every bit of advice worth getting, for which there was time.

The indications are that personal judgments of this sort continued for many years to play an unusually important part in major AEC contract decisions. Thus, from what is presently known, the decisions to contract with Western Electric for the operation of the Sandia Laboratory, with Du Pont for the management of Savannah River, with the University of California for the operation of Livermore, and with Westinghouse for the development of submarine reactors were, like the major contract decisions of World War II, essentially "closed circle" decisions of a few key individuals up to and including the President. The President's intervention itself signified that the national interest was paramount, and that the routine procedure of picking a contractor by inviting competitive bids should be set aside.[29] The number of qualified organizations and individuals was still too small to allow a wide range of significant choice, while the (military or political) penalties of delay often dictated a kind of inner cabinet action hardly desirable or equitable in most contract awards by most government agencies.

It is no reflection on the integrity of the public officials responsible for these actions to suggest that their judgment, based inevitably on their more or less limited personal knowledge and experience, should, wherever possible, be checked out against the knowledge and experience of agency staff, augmented by fresh information on the qualifications of potential contractors gained through some equitable and systematic procedure. That, of course, is what is usually achieved by the normal process of contractor se-

[29] Thus, by letter of May 13, 1949 to Leroy Wilson, president of the American Telephone and Telegraph Co., President Truman asked the Bell Telephone Laboratories to accept a contract for the management of the AEC's Sandia Laboratory in the following words:

"This operation, which is a vital segment of the atomic weapons program, is of extreme importance and urgency in the national defense, and should have the best possible technical direction.

"I hope that after you have heard more in detail from the Atomic Energy Commission, your organization will find it possible to undertake this task. In my opinion you have here an opportunity to render an exceptional service in the national interest." (From photocopy of the original letter kindly provided by the Sandia Laboratory.)

lection set forth in government regulations. As the number of experienced organizations and scientists in the nuclear field grows and the pressure of military needs relaxes, the award of operating contracts by the AEC can be expected to approximate more closely to this model (as it has evidently done in the recent round of operating contractor selections at Hanford and Idaho Falls).

This is not to assert that the model was never observed during the Commission's first decade[30] and should always be observed during its second, or that any amount of staff work can obviate the exercise of human judgment upon which contract awards must ultimately rest. " . . . we . . . cut quickly to the heart of the problem—the job to be done and what firms were best qualified . . . to undertake these tasks," observed one defender of earlier AEC procedures, and more than one commentator has noted the waste of money and motion involved in such an excessively systematic and insufficiently discriminating procedure as that which, in 1965, netted some 126 proposals for the site of a projected 200-bev accelerator, 85 of which were judged to meet the AEC's announced criteria.[31] The ideal system of contractor selection must combine fairness with common sense; encourage genuine, not spurious, competition; and provide enough relevant information for responsible officials to decide which proposal is most likely to advance the agency's programmatic and policy objectives.

What *Does* an Operating Contractor Contribute?

It has often been contended that changing the contractor operating an AEC facility in fact changes very little, for most personnel go on doing what they did before and merely receive their paychecks from a different employer (though the money itself, of course, continues to come from the U. S. Treasury). In fact, the stability of personnel during changes of operating contractors has been used as an argument for not changing contractors. Most

[30] Thus, the 1952 selection of Goodyear to operate the gaseous diffusion plant at Portsmouth or the 1950 selection of Phillips to operate the Idaho Falls reactor test site were pointed to as a model of meticulous staff work, in which a careful and thorough technical analysis of bids preceded the final choice.

[31] "The New Accelerator," *Science* (Sept. 24, 1965), p. 1484; and "Accelerator Competition," *Science* (Nov. 19, 1965), p. 1005.

staff have remained put during the earlier contractor changes about which information is available (Table 5), and the AEC has done what it can to reduce turnover during the departure of General Electric at Hanford, even requiring, as a condition of the contract award, that the incoming contractor retain as many as possible of the existing personnel.[32] A similar position was adopted during the change of contractors at Idaho Falls:

> The AEC . . . recognizes that continued successful operation at the NRTS [National Reactor Testing Station] is largely dependent upon the highly skilled and trained scientific, technical, and craft personnel who have so effectively served in the activities to be transferred. Accordingly, the AEC, Phillips, and the new contractor when selected will make every effort to minimize dislocation of workers and it is expected that most employees involved in the functions to be transferred will have the opportunity to transfer to the new contractor. In accordance with AEC policy, support will be given to efforts designed to protect the status and interests of employees who transfer.[33]

However, the number of staff taken by a departing contractor is more an indication of his alternative opportunities at the time and his sense of responsibility to the government than of the extent of his contribution to the AEC program. No doubt, the managerial contribution of different contractors has varied not only with their competence but with circumstances. During World War II, neither the business manager (who signed paychecks), nor the Regents, nor the officers of the University of California were permitted to visit Los Alamos, for whose management they were supposedly responsible;[34] and the range of freedom granted a con-

[32] E.g., the request for an expression of interest from industry in the operation of the Hanford chemical processing facilities stated, "Since there presently exists a complement of highly trained personnel, trained at Hanford at AEC expense, it would be expected that the new contractor would exert its best efforts to employ such personnel. The present operating contractor has agreed to use all appropriate efforts to encourage this labor and supervisory force to remain at Hanford as it represents an important National asset. . . . a prerequisite to the selection of a contractor would be . . . the willingness of the company to exert strong effort to retain trained plant work forces and necessary service personnel." AEC, Richland Operations Office (April 3, 1964).

[33] "AEC to Offer Other Organizations Opportunity to Perform Contract Work at NRTS," AEC press release (Feb. 5, 1965).

[34] See Robert A. Dahl and Ralph S. Brown, *Domestic Control of Atomic Energy* (Social Science Research Council, 1951), p. 83, footnote 4, and David E. Lilienthal,

TABLE 5

Employee Stability During Operating Contractor Changes

Facility	Date of Change	Contractor		Number of Employees	
		Old	New	Total	Leaving with Old Contractor
Hanford	1946	Du Pont	General Electric	3,950	135
Oak Ridge (Y-12)	1947	Tennessee-Eastman	Union Carbide	1,800	12
Oak Ridge (X-10)	1948	Monsanto	Union Carbide	2,300	8
Idaho Falls	1953	American Cyanamid	Phillips Petroleum	300	15
Pacific Northwest Lab.[a]	1965	General Electric	Battelle	1,984	13

Source: First four lines, *AEC Authorizing Legislation Fiscal Year 1963*, Hearings before the Subcommittee on Legislation of the Joint Committee on Atomic Energy, 1962, pp. 406-7; last line, Sept. 2, 1965 letter from S. L. Fawcett, laboratory director.
[a] Formerly Hanford Laboratories. Of the thirteen employees who did not transfer to Battelle, only four remained with G.E.

tractor in a tightly controlled and classified development program (like naval reactors) is clearly more limited than in an open research program with no hard schedule of technical objectives. But, overall, the doctrine that contractors have contributed little of significance to the management of nuclear programs (which is often associated with the view that the contract is merely a device to avoid civil service regulations and pay scales while maintaining government controls) is as unacceptable as the contrary doctrine (which has achieved a certain vogue recently, particularly with regard to the so-called "military-industrial complex") that contractors have dominated government nuclear policies.

Undoubtedly a principal contribution of contractors has been the services of industrialists, scientists, engineers, and administrators of great and, in many cases, unique experience and ability. For, in the management of many of its critical facilities, the AEC has enlisted some of the nation's leading universities and companies—notably, the Universities of California and Chicago, and those banded together as Associated Universities; Du Pont, General Electric, Westinghouse, and the AT&T-Western Electric-Bell Laboratories complex.

Also important has been the definable set of working conditions —pay scales, not always so peripheral personnel benefits, administrative structure and procedures—and the less definable but no less important tempo, philosophy or atmosphere established by an industrial or academic employer. Indeed, insofar as *some* characteristically industrial or academic working conditions cannot be identified at an AEC facility, one may conclude that the Commission has failed to achieve a fundamental objective of the managerial contract: to bring private talents and methods to bear on a goal set by the government. It is the recurrent complaint of responsible and able contractors that the growth of government controls and regulations has made it difficult for them to achieve this objective. However, it can also be argued that the objective

Change, Hope, and the Bomb, op. cit., p. 77. Robert Oppenheimer has observed that, "The contractor [at Los Alamos] during the war years was an extremely helpful and able contractor, but was really distinguished primarily by his absence. Since then the university has been allowed to take a somewhat more active part." *Investigation into the United States Atomic Energy Project,* Hearings before the Joint Committee on Atomic Energy (1949), Pt. 7, p. 304.

is, at least in part, unattainable: that, as a government agency
cannot turn over *complete* responsibility for the management of a
government facility to a private organization, so it cannot fail to
impose requirements which will *somewhat* impair the freedom
and modify the character of private management. The management that emerges from this interplay of private standards with
government requirements can be neither purely private nor purely public, but a meld of both. The question is just what the nature of this meld should be. Overly tight controls, which many
contractors assert have been imposed in recent years, reduce the
special contribution a private organization can make to the
fulfillment of a government mission; overly loose controls pose
the contrary danger that the government's interest will be con-
founded with that of the private organization.

The contractor's contributions have been effected by the assignment of senior staff of the contractor's home organization (often,
but not always, specified during contract negotiations) to the AEC
facility at the outset of the contract term; the subsequent movement of selected (in the case of contractors with sharp fluctuations
in workload, like Pratt & Whitney, and Holmes & Narver, of substantial numbers of) personnel between the two organizations;
and the continuing visits, communications, advice, and services
provided by headquarters to the contract facility on technical
matters, legal issues, purchasing, labor relations, and so forth.
However, a number of factors often lead to an attenuation of such
contacts and services (and the resultant degree of administrative
isolation of the contract organization furnishes the factual basis
for the common, but generally mistaken, charge that the contractor therefore contributes little of value to the management of the
government facility). These include: the physical isolation of
many sites; the decentralization and delegation of authority normal
to many academic and industrial organizations; the need to segre-
gate costs payable by the government and to prevent any covert
subsidy of private activity; the need to serve the government's
programmatic interests rather than those of the contractor; and, a
point often neglected, the desire on the part of both AEC and the
contractor to avoid any real or apparent conflict between the contractor's private and government responsibilities.

Because of this common separation of operating contract responsibilities from the contractor's other activities, the choice of a director is a critical element in a contractor's contribution to the management of an AEC facility. After paying due deference to the familiarity of universities with basic research and of industry with large scale technical development, some knowledgeable AEC staff assert that the character of the director is more important than the profit-making or nonprofit status of the contractor in determining the effectiveness or, in more general terms, the "spirit" of a laboratory.

One of the key contributions of an operating contractor is his freedom of action. The president of a major company or university can deal directly and frankly, as the situation requires, with the president of another institution, a senator, a journalist, the Secretary of a Department, the Chairman of the Commission, or a scientist in or out of government; and corresponding freedom is enjoyed at other levels by other contractor staff. This freedom of speech, operation, and maneuver is the unique asset of private status that cannot be (or, at any event, has not been) fully shared by responsible government officials and civil servants. If it is being eroded, as some observers charge, then the operating contractors' staff will indeed become merely another and unacknowledged kind of civil servant.[35]

The value of this asset and the nature of a contractor's responsibility for the operation of an AEC installation is plainly manifested during contract negotiations and at times of crisis. Peak demands at the contract site may be met by drawing personnel from other contractor branches or the open market; and the contractor's principal officers, directors, and trustees will be actively engaged in coping with the crisis. ("These laboratories want to be

[35] Cf. Bruce Smith's account of how Albert Wohlstetter and others at RAND communicated directly to top Air Force officers, in 1952-53, the findings of a study that led to a major redeployment of Strategic Air Command planes and bases. "It is doubtful whether an Air Force officer, an 'in-house' advisory group made up of Air Force career personnel, or even a civilian advisory group attached to a unit within the normal chain of command, would have the same opportunity or incentive to by-pass immediate superiors and press for the adoption of controversial ideas at higher levels." Bruce L. R. Smith, *The Rand Corporation* (Harvard University Press, Cambridge, Mass., 1966), p. 226.

independent—until they're in trouble, and then they come to you for help," a university president remarked.) For, despite the risk-free provisions inserted in critical contracts with the personal approval of the President, there can be little doubt that the good name and reputation of a contractor is at stake in the quality of his contract performance, and that if, for example, a radioactive cloud should cross Chicago as the result of a reactor catastrophe at Argonne, the University of Chicago, its president and trustees would, rightly or wrongly, suffer for it; or if an American nuclear bomb were to explode accidentally anywhere in the world, the (moral, if not economic) repercussions would be felt not only by the American government, but by the Sandia Corporation, and the directors and officers of Western Electric and the American Telephone and Telegraph Company.[36] If the good name of an operating contractor were all that he contributed to the management of a laboratory, that would be a significant contribution—provided, to be sure, that the contractor has a name worthy of preservation. The success of the AEC's new order of operating contractors will hinge to no small extent upon the degree to which this virtue of the old order can be retained.

[36] Cf. General Groves: ". . . there was never any question in any of our minds but that du Pont would suffer staggering losses if a major disaster should ever occur. The damage that it would have sustained could not have been measured in dollars lost; all such losses were to be borne by the government. But the damage to its reputation and consequently, to its future welfare, would have been untold, and the directors . . . who had agreed to undertake the work would have been completely discredited." *Now It Can Be Told* (Harper & Brothers, New York, 1962), p. 59.

CHAPTER III

The Private and Public Sectors

Industrial vs. Academic Managers

That AEC's production plants and development laboratories should be operated by industry and its fundamental research laboratories by universities—i.e., that each installation should be managed by organizations and men most familiar with the kind of task at hand—seems natural and sensible. And, broadly speaking, this has been the aim of Commission policy.

But the actual situation that has developed over two decades and, therefore, the concrete alternatives faced by the AEC in R&D contracting are not always so simple. On the one hand, laboratories managed by universities have scarcely confined themselves to basic research but, both at their own initiative and at the government's request, have from the outset undertaken (or subsequently pushed into) major programs of applied research and the development of new prototypes, processes, and products; on the other hand, industry-managed laboratories with such a specific practical assignment as developing a type of reactor or improving a production process have broadened their scope and undertaken fundamental scientific research in a variety of fields. At the Sandia, Oak Ridge, and Hanford laboratories, academic and industrial, nonprofit and profit-making managers have alternated. The industry-managed Oak Ridge National Laboratory is pioneering important programs of pure research in molecular biology, while the university-managed Argonne National Laboratory has initiated countless important developments in reactor technology. All told, there has been considerable untidiness in the assignment of R&D program and managerial responsibilities to different kinds of contractors—which is largely as it should be, since the special capacities of individual laboratories and contractors are determined by their (past and current) history, and history is not very tidy. Accordingly, as AEC Chairman Seaborg has observed, "use is made of whatever source . . . appears best suited to accomplish the particular research and development task at hand. . . ."[1] The conclusion that the technical qualifications of a laboratory are more significant criteria for government contracting than are general administrative or ideological considerations was also reached by the Bell Report, which recommended that "Choices among available [managerial] arrangements should be based primarily on . . . Relative effectiveness and efficiency and Avoidance of conflicts of interest."[2]

Government vs. Private Laboratories

Yet this pragmatic philosophy has bred long-term dilemmas. It may be cheaper to assign a particular R&D program to a laboratory in which the government has invested hundreds of millions of dollars over the last two decades; but is the AEC doing all it should to fulfill its statutory responsibility of promoting a competitive nuclear industry when so large a proportion of its funds allocated by these criteria remain concentrated at a few government laboratories?[3] Gross statistics show that, during the last dec-

[1] Progress report on AEC implementation of Bell Report recommendations, accompanying letter from Chairman Seaborg to the Director, Bureau of the Budget, Oct. 16, 1962 (Multilith), p. 2.

[2] *Report to the President on Government Contracting for Research and Development*, Prepared by the Bureau of the Budget and Referred to the Committee on Government Operations, U. S. Senate (May 17, 1962), p. 10.

[3] ". . . although great benefits have come to the Commission through its policy of contracting out the management of its facilities to private groups, this practice has made it difficult for truly competitive privately-owned facilities to compete with these Government facilities. To . . . take on new work in the Government plants can usually be done at a lower cost than by private industry and, thus, private industry is essentially competing with incremental Government costs." Ernest B. Tremmel, Di-

TABLE 6

AEC R&D Obligations by Sector in Recent Years

Sector	1966[a]	1965	1964	1963	1959	1955[a]
	Millions of Dollars					
Profit-making organizations	$ 736	$ 743	$ 740	$ 650	$449	$140
Nonprofit organizations	523	490	471	410	237	105
All organizations	$1,259	$1,233	$1,211	$1,060	$686	$245
Profit-making research centers[b]	$387	$386	$390	$334	$299	$ 95
Nonprofit research centers[b]	440	416	401	342	202	86
All research centers[b]	$827	$802	$790	$676	$501	$181
	Percentage Distribution (All Organizations = 100)					
Profit-making organizations	58	60	61	61	65	57
Nonprofit organizations	42	40	39	39	35	43
All organizations	100	100	100	100	100	100
Profit-making research centers[b]	31	31	32	32	44	39
Nonprofit research centers[b]	35	34	33	32	29	35
All research centers[b]	66	65	65	64	73	74

Source: National Science Foundation, *Federal Funds for Science*, and *Federal Funds for Research, Development and Other Scientific Activities*, various years.

[a] Estimated.

[b] "Research centers," as defined by the Foundation, are roughly comparable to major government-owned, contractor-operated laboratories. However, the list of AEC research centers given in *Federal Funds for Research, Development, and Other Scientific Activities*, Vol. XII, 1964, p. 102, excludes such major laboratories as Hanford, Savannah River, and Evendale, while including smaller biomedical research projects at a number of universities.

ade, roughly three-fifths of its R&D contract obligations have been going to profit-making organizations (Table 6). But:

1. The two-fifths which have gone to nonprofit organizations were a phenomenally high proportion compared to the 5-10 percent or so of Department of Defense or NASA research and development contract expenditures that have been so allocated in recent years.[4] This is attributable in part to the special role played

rector, AEC Division of Industrial Participation, Remarks before the Third Annual Meeting of the Institute of Nuclear Materials Management (St. Louis, May 14, 1962).

[4] Nonprofit institutions received 8 percent of the Defense Department's R&D expenditures in 1963 and 9 percent in 1964; 10 percent of NASA's R&D expenditures in 1963, and 5 percent in 1964. From data reported in *Federal Funds for Research, Development, and Other Scientific Activities*, National Science Foundation, Vol. XIII (1965), pp. 126-27 and Vol. XIV (1965), pp. 86-87.

by university scientists and university-managed laboratories in the birth of the nuclear age, which has persisted during its maturation; to the responsibility for fundamental research in nuclear sciences assigned to the AEC before, and reaffirmed after, the creation of the National Science Foundation; and to the exercise by university-managed laboratories like Los Alamos, Livermore, and Argonne of some functions performed for other government agencies by their "inhouse" laboratories.

2. R&D funds have remained concentrated predominantly at government-owned (if privately managed) facilities, although, over the years, a somewhat larger proportion has gone into private laboratories (Tables 6 and 10).

Industry itself seems to have been more divided about the direction that AEC policy should take in this matter (or the pace at which it should proceed) than might be expected, since firms with massive operating contracts have not been eager to see their volume reduced. To be more precise, the company branch responsible for managing an AEC facility has not been eager, since there can be a visible difference of outlook within the same company between a vice president for nuclear operations and a vice president for commercial operations. On at least one notable occasion, the chairman of the Commission received letters from several companies informing him that the head of their nuclear division did *not* necessarily speak for the company.

In his September 1959 directive to the heads of executive agencies stating that "the Federal Government will not . . . provide a service or product for its own use if such product or service can be procured from private enterprise through ordinary business channels," President Eisenhower's Budget Director Maurice Stans recognized that, "Even the operation of a Government-owned facility by a private organization through contractual arrangement does not automatically assure that the Government is not competing with private enterprise. This type of arrangement could act as a barrier to the development and growth of competitive commercial sources and procurement through ordinary business channels."[5] In December, the U. S. Chamber of Commerce, the National Associ-

[5] Bureau of the Budget Bulletin 60-62, "Commercial industrial activities of the government providing products or services for government use" (Sept. 21, 1959).

ation of Manufacturers, and the Manufacturing Chemists' Association took the occasion of Stans' statement to detail, in separate communications to AEC Chairman John McCone, numerous activities that appeared to conflict with this policy. Citing many examples of R&D, design work, fabrication, and services performed by AEC laboratories (including four managed by universities as well as three managed by industry) that warranted review under this policy, the Chamber declared that:

Research and development work should be conducted in private facilities, except where it is clearly demonstrated that such are unavailable for a particular job. The policy of the Government should be to fully utilize and encourage the growth of industrial capacity rather than according preference to Government facilities.[6]

In his reply, Acting Commission Chairman John Floberg accepted the general policy of contracting with private *competitive* industry for all possible goods and services but rejected its applicability to the specific cases cited for a variety of reasons: the absence of industrial capacity; the Commission's obligation to avoid fostering a single source of supply or service; the undesirability of subcontracting an activity closely integrated with a contractor's operations; the impracticality or expense of contracting for sporadic needs and, more generally, for unstandardized products and services still under development. He noted, further, that the determination of whether to contract or subcontract with private industry for goods and services was made by the AEC and the prime contractor "in accordance with normal private industrial criteria, modified to the extent necessary to comply with existing AEC directives and applicable Federal law."[7] Acting AEC Chairman John S. Graham drove this point home more painfully in a subsequent letter to the Chamber of Commerce:

[6] See letter of Jack Abernathy (Chairman, Committee on Commercial Uses of Atomic Energy, Chamber of Commerce of the United States) and attachment, Dec. 7, 1959, in *The Future Role of the Atomic Energy Commission Laboratories*, Joint Committee on Atomic Energy, 86 Cong. 2 sess. (October 1960), pp. 269-70. One reader at a national laboratory reported that he could compile an equally long list of cases in which his laboratory had tried to contract with industry for R&D but, failing to find the competence, had had to do the work itself.

[7] See *The Future Role of the Atomic Energy Commission Laboratories*, op. cit., pp. 251-68.

. . . I think the Chamber has a problem with industry itself, mainly as large companies operate our large Government-owned installations. The attitude of our cost plus a fixed fee contractors, who perform much of the procurement for the Commission, does affect the extent to which other private industry can have the opportunity to do some of the work. In other words, you might examine to what extent a large company operating an AEC-owned facility can foster work to be done by private industry, other than in the AEC-owned facility.[8]

Recognizing the truth of Graham's thrust, the Chamber established what some called a "reciprocal trade committee," which included representatives of companies operating both a government and a private nuclear facility, to explore the advantages that a firm might derive from reducing or relinquishing its operating contract responsibilities and receiving more work (competitively awarded) in its own facilities. The efforts of such private groups, of those portions of the AEC sympathetic to their goals, and of the Joint Committee on Atomic Energy (JCAE) have led to a sequence of recent events fostering the conduct in private facilities of nuclear activities formerly confined to government installations. Notable among these have been the establishment of a private nuclear fuel processing plant in New York, the passage of legislation authorizing the private ownership of fissionable material, the restriction of architect-engineer design work in government facilities, and the encouragement of private work in government property at Hanford. And, of course, a similar chain of events leading to the gradual establishment of a private industrial and academic capacity for nuclear research, development, fabrication, and services can be traced back to the inception of the AEC and was accentuated after passage of the 1954 Atomic Energy Act.

There has never been any doubt about the policy of the Commission and the Congress of promoting a private nuclear industry. Doubts have arisen only about the economic practicality, the timing, and the means of doing so in particular technological areas; the prices that should be paid in direct and indirect government subsidies and R&D expenditures; and how a truly competitive industry can ultimately be created in a field with a limited

---

[8] From a Jan. 27, 1961, letter of Graham to the Chamber of Commerce Committee on Commercial Uses of Atomic Energy.

initial private market, substantial capital requirements, exceptional and expensive demands for technical reliability, and government licensing, regulation, and control of critical facilities, materials, and information.

In the domain of civilian technology, the Commission's contract policies (and the contract awards which implement them) have been directed toward two frequently contradictory objectives: the development of nuclear technology that can be manufactured and sold by private companies on its merit in free and unsubsidized competition with alternative products of conventional technology; and the promotion of a nuclear industry within which free competition also reigns. The reconciliation of these objectives has been particularly difficult in the field of civilian power reactors, whose commercial acceptability depends not only on their economy calculated to several decimal places[9] but on electric utilities' confidence in the manufacturers' ability to guarantee their performance. That confidence is based not only on the technical virtues of a reactor but on the experience, size, and financial strength of its manufacturer.

At one time Westinghouse and at another time General Electric has appeared predominant in the private nuclear power industry, as they have been predominant in the conventional power industry; but at no time has any "third echelon" company—Allis-Chalmers, Atomics International, Babcock & Wilcox, Combustion Engineering, or General Atomics—superseded them. Speaking in 1965, at a time of apparent G.E. domination, an employee of one of the latter companies observed that the Commission was torn between its wish to promote these "weaker sisters" and recognition that G.E. was best qualified to bring nuclear power to immediate commercial application. Repeatedly, G.E. would proffer arrangements so attractive AEC staff called it "the generous electric company"; but, after contracting for them, they would bemoan the consequences for a competitive nuclear industry.

If a real "third force" is to emerge, he argued, the AEC must pick a third echelon company and back its advanced reactor concept. This the Commission has been reluctant to do, in order to

[9] Some of the assumptions upon which these calculations are based are so gross, the decimal places are "a joke in the fraternity," one reader observes.

avoid the onus of a choice that might make one company but break the others. Instead, it has given most of the work on developing advanced reactors to the national laboratories, assuming that, when they *are* developed, private industry will adopt them. However, to market a reactor successfully, a company must be thoroughly familiar with the knowledge ("pure" as well as practical) and experience gained in the development of its components; only thus can the long-term technical performance and economics of the final system be appraised. Even in the established field of water reactors, the basic drawings of which are all in the public domain, other companies have been unable to challenge G.E. and Westinghouse, because they lack the experience and the people to back up the drawings.

It appears likely that the nuclear industry will, for a good many years, retain its special, closely regulated, and, in key segments, oligopolistic character.[10] Within these limitations, imposed largely by technological and economic factors and the vast investment that has already been made in public facilities, a private industry with a significant R&D capability is gradually being established.

[10] "This, then, is the enigma of antitrust in the atomic energy field. The nature of the risks involved, coupled with the expense, require the efforts of large companies, or the combined efforts of small ones. There is a notable social good to be derived from getting the job done, particularly when the international implications of the struggle for usable atomic power are considered. Yet the penalty of success may be an antitrust prosecution, resulting in loss of license and patent rights. Even before that state is reached, a company may be restricted in its contractual operations with the Atomic Energy Commission because of the policy of spreading the business and helping the small entrepreneur. There is a game called 'Monopoly' which may have an unrecognized verisimilitude: Once the game reached the point where one player or even two were successful in putting hotels on the better streets, the players usually broke up the game, divided the money and the property, and started over. There was no fun in playing against overwhelming odds. To prolong the game, one had to exercise care not to reach a point of domination." Richard Cosway, "Antitrust Provisions of the Atomic Energy Act," *Vanderbilt Law Review,* Vol. 12 (1959), p. 194.

CHAPTER IV

Big Science and the Universities

Of the two R&D functions performed for the AEC by universities, the conduct of relatively small scale research projects by university faculty and the management of major research facilities by one or more institutions, we will be concerned in this chapter with the second, since "big science" not only consumes far more AEC funds than "small science" but raises more heated policy questions.

The value of "small nuclear science," financed mainly by fixed-price contracts with universities for research by faculty on ideas they have usually originated,[1] is evident: it provides nuclear science and technology with a stream of fresh ideas, information, and talent from universities throughout the country. The main problem faced by these programs is how to support new proposals of merit within an increasingly stable budget that tends to be absorbed in the extension of existing projects. Those on the giving and receiving ends of the program would, of course, like to avoid the problem by continuing budgetary increases; the alternative solution, which budgetary restraints have periodically imposed, is the painful sacrifice of less meritorious research.

[1] For 1963, the AEC has reported that 1,397 research contracts with universities and other nonprofit organizations resulted from unsolicited proposals and only 10 from solicited proposals. *Government and Science,* Hearings before the Subcommittee on Science, Research and Development of the House Science and Astronautics Committee, 88 Cong. 2 sess. (May and June 1964), No. 4, p. 170.

Contracting with universities for the management of major basic research facilities built and operated with public funds has posed problems of locating the facility, determining if it should be managed as a "national facility" by one university or a group of universities, and ensuring equitable access to the machine by nonresident scientists. Something more should be said about each problem.

Locating Unique Facilities[2]

As the expense of building and operating machines for fundamental nuclear research (notably, to accelerate various elementary particles to relatively low or to the highest possible energies; special research reactors; and devices for research into nuclear fusion) has risen, the determination of the best site for each instrument has become more important and more hotly debated. Unfortunately, purely technical considerations such as the availability of land, power, water, air, and transportation (and, in the case of the proposed 200-bev accelerator, the AEC has added proximity to "a commercial and industrial center which includes research and development activities," and adequate "housing, cultural and educational facilities for some 2,000 scientific and technical personnel and their families")[3] do not narrow the range of choice sufficiently to escape serious problems of politics, economics, and morale.

[2] A reader first asked for and then volunteered a definition of "unique facility": one that cannot readily be purchased from or built by commercial fabricators with a record of fabricating similar facilities, but must be designed and developed individually, and is so costly and special-purpose that more than one of a precise kind is rarely built in the nation.

[3] "AEC-NAS Enter Agreement on Evaluating Sites for a Proposed New National Accelerator Laboratory," AEC press release, April 28, 1965. An attachment, "Considerations Involved in Siting a Major New Accelerator," supplied the following explanation: "Proximity to a commercial industrial center which includes adequate coverage of special needs in electronics, electrical and precision mechanical equipment will ease problems of recruiting technical support and in obtaining specialized supplies. Proximity to other broadly based research and development activities will provide opportunities for desirable interaction of scientific and engineering personnel. . . . Proximity to a cultural center that includes a large university will provide intellectual and cultural opportunities attractive for staff and families." The last point was elaborated in site criteria for a large accelerator proposed in December 1962 by Brookhaven staff: "The machine should be located in a region that will seem desirable to wives

The political heat engendered by conflicts over the location of expensive facilities has been manifest. Thus, in the summer of 1963, the entire Indiana delegation petitioned President Kennedy, and a Midwest delegation headed by Senator Hubert Humphrey called to endorse the construction of a 12.5-bev accelerator at Madison, Wisconsin. Privately, some of the region's congressmen bitterly castigated the President's science adviser, Jerome Wiesner, for his allegedly adverse recommendation on this machine[4] and what they regarded as a cabal of scientists and politicians from the two coasts against the interests of the Midwest; twelve midwestern governors have since demanded that the 200-bev accelerator be located in their region.[5] The economic is-

---

and families, since many families will have to be uprooted to assemble the staff. Well qualified men may refuse to join the staff if the location seems undesirable to their wives or if available facilities for education of their children seem inadequate." See *AEC Authorizing Legislation Fiscal Year 1966,* Hearings before the Joint Committee on Atomic Energy, 89 Cong. 1 sess., Pt. 1 (1965), p. 390.

[4] The full facts on this painful episode are not yet in the public domain. Donald Fleming, a Cambridge historian who may just possibly have obtained this account from a Cambridge source, has reported that in November 1963, Senator Humphrey "felt optimistic that the President [Kennedy] was about to commit himself . . . to the MURA [i.e., the Midwest Universities Research Association's proposed 12.5-bev] accelerator . . ." but that, following the assassination that month, "President Johnson asked . . . Wiesner . . . to prepare a memorandum stating the case against MURA. It does not follow that this was Wiesner's own position. When, just before Christmas [1963], the President met with a group from MURA, he read from this hostile memorandum prepared by Wiesner's office on his own instructions and told the dumbfounded MURA people where it had come from. Then the President dismissed them without any opportunity for rebuttals. . . . The MURA people stamped out of the White House denouncing Wiesner as an agent of the bloated East and vowing in retaliation to block any accelerators on the East or West coasts." Donald Fleming, "The Big Money and High Politics of Science," *The Atlantic* (August 1965), p. 43. This version corresponds with one we received from a creditable authority who added that the lethal blow was struck not by Wiesner but by that silent guardian of the public purse, the Bureau of the Budget. Cf. also the account of these events given by D. S. Greenberg in *Science* (Jan. 31, 1964), pp. 450-52.

[5] "Midwestern Governors today demanded that a proposed $280 million nuclear accelerator be located in the Midwest and accused the Federal Government of discrimination in allocation of aerospace and research centers.

"Michigan's Gov. George Romney, chairman of the 12-member Governors' Conference, called on them to plead personally their case to the Atomic Energy Commission.

" 'We have been discriminated against continually,' said Ohio Gov. James A. Rhodes. 'We're not asking for something here. We're entitled to it.' " See "A-Installation Demanded for Midwest," *Washington Post* (Sept. 21, 1965).

A proposal to locate the accelerator in the Midwest was submitted to the AEC in

sues, of course, are not confined to the palpable benefits to local business and employment (and, in the case of big accelerators, electric utilities and their suppliers), but extend to the broader (real and/or fancied) cultural and economic stimulus that a major R&D center may bring to an area.

Finally, the AEC cannot ignore the effects of site decisions on morale at existing laboratories. Nor does it. At one laboratory visited by an august committee of physicists designated to advise on the merit and location of a proposed machine, it was observed that the committee commenced with strictly technical questions but "got down to personalities in the end," and to the possible effects of a negative decision upon the machine's proponents and laboratory morale. On more than one occasion persons who have read the letters in which the advice of leading physicists about the scientific desirability of building an accelerator has been privately conveyed to the government have sardonically noted a strange relationship between the location of the machine's designers, that of the adviser, and the nature of his advice. The contention of various laboratories for major new facilities and programs is part of their effort to introduce exciting new work and talent to maintain a vitality endangered by nuclear test restrictions, the political uncertainties that becloud the future of nuclear weaponry, production cutbacks, budgetary restraints, and the general erosion of age.

Other arguments for putting a research facility at an existing laboratory are that it can be done more cheaply and quickly than creating a new laboratory, using existing equipment, services, and staff (top and middle management, scientists, engineers, accountants, secretaries, skilled and unskilled labor) on a full or part-time basis during the design, development, and construction phases. Counter arguments are the constantly growing size and complexity of existing laboratories, and their inability to give to any single program the concentrated attention and fresh outlook that can be supplied by a new organization created *à nouveau*

October 1965 by the Midwest Resources Association, whose steering committee consists of twelve governors, six senators, and six representatives from the Midwest, including Melvin Price of the Joint Committee.

(like the national laboratory proposed for the 200-bev accelerator) or grafted on to a university and utilizing some of its services (like the Stanford accelerator).

Regional factors had been explicitly considered by the Army and, subsequently, the infant Commission, in their decision to sponsor major basic research available to universities in four regions: the West, at the Berkeley Radiation Laboratory, which had been functioning since before World War II;[6] the Midwest, at what became in 1946 the Argonne National Laboratory, an outgrowth of the critical work conducted at the University of Chicago during the war; the Northeast, at the Brookhaven National Laboratory; and the South, at the Oak Ridge Institute of Nuclear Studies. All of these sites were approved first by General Groves in 1946 and later endorsed by the AEC.

A great machine cannot be dismembered, and siting decisions which are tortuous personally and politically will have to be made. However, some of the torture might be reduced and the broader interests of the nation advanced by three general measures:

1. Provision of adequate funds for visitor travel, housing, and auxiliary expenses in the budget of a research facility, rendering its resources more widely accessible.

2. Clarification (by the President and the Congress) of national policy about the weight that should be given to regional factors in the allocation of government R&D expenditures, and particularly expenditures for basic research.

One step in this direction was the September 14, 1965, memorandum of President Johnson instructing the heads of departments and agencies, in part, to give "consideration, where research capability of comparable quality exists, to awarding grants and contracts to [educational] institutions not now heavily engaged in federal research programs . . . . when indicated [agencies] should use a larger proportion of their research funds in accordance with the intent of the policy." However, the memorandum nowhere explicitly stated

[6] A new, multi-university managed installation could not have been set up either in the San Francisco or Los Angeles area, one witness noted, because of the rivalry between the California Institute of Technology and Berkeley; "it would have had to be in the middle."

that regional (as distinct from institutional) factors should be taken into account, so that Senator Gaylord Nelson's earlier observation that "We don't have any definite national policy today on the [regional] pattern to be followed in allocating Federal funds for research and development" retains much force. Congress's declaration in the National Aeronautics and Space Administration (NASA) Authorization Act of 1966 was plainer in purpose if not method: "It is the sense of Congress that it is in the national interest that consideration be given to geographical distribution of Federal research funds whenever feasible, and that the National Aeronautics and Space Administration should explore ways and means of distributing its research and development funds whenever feasible."[7]

3. Preparation of a comprehensive, annual statement of projected government investments in major scientific facilities.

Such a statement should improve both the factual and the political basis for the rational geographic distribution of these facilities, since a negative decision by the AEC on one installation might be counterbalanced by a positive decision on another by, for example, NASA. In high energy physics, several such statements have been prepared by the AEC, aided by the National Science Foundation (NSF) and the President's Science Advisory Committee, but the regional factor has been muted when it could have been made explicit and extended to other agencies and other fields of science. To be sure, the location of, let us say, an optical telescope and an arid zone research center in a particular region, in lieu of an accelerator, will not make that region's physicists any happier (though it may placate their legislators). As, whatever the Executive may propose, the patron committees of the Congress will eventually dispose, there are evident limits to the effectiveness of interagency regional planning for science. But these limits have yet to be reached. A yearly capital-and-regional budget for science, accompanying the President's annual budget message, might dampen regional struggles by introducing better knowledge and fuller rationality into the allocation process; and it

[7] "Memorandum from the President to the Heads of Departments and Agencies," The White House (Sept. 14, 1965); Congressional Record, Senate (Sept. 29, 1964), daily ed., p. 22355; and Public Law 89-53, 89 Cong., H.R. 7717 (June 28, 1965), Sec. 5.

could usefully be supplemented by such longer-term plans and projections as can be made with any show of confidence.

Multifoliate Management

Until recently, there was a striking contrast between the AEC practice of contracting with one university for the management of large basic research facilities (notably, the Lawrence Radiation Laboratory at Berkeley, the Stanford Linear Accelerator Center, the Ames Laboratory, and the Argonne National Laboratory) and the National Science Foundation pattern of contracting for this purpose exclusively with organizations representing a number of universities (Associated Universities, Inc., the Association of Universities for Research in Astronomy, and the University Corporation for Atmospheric Research).

NSF's policy has been abetted by two circumstances: its facilities have been built from scratch at fresh locations, unlike the foregoing AEC laboratories whose nucleus had existed at the institution with which the AEC subsequently contracted for an expanded program; and they were, from the outset, more a product of inter-institutional committee planning than were these AEC laboratories. The principal successful example of multi-university management of an AEC basic research facility, Brookhaven, followed (or, rather, pioneered) the NSF pattern of corporate planning, as did the dual-university management adopted for the Harvard-MIT and Princeton-Pennsylvania accelerators.

Critics assert that the National Science Foundation practice produces a "characterless" or "service" facility with which scientists have no sense of identification; ". . . this is the vogue today—everyone wants to get into the act," said an official of one great university scornfully. "Everything must fit a pattern; the government can't tolerate individuality." An eminent physicist contrasted the reputation of the NSF observatories unfavorably with that of the Palomar Observatory, though whether such a difference in standing (if true) should be attributed to the mode of management is dubious.

Such comments are far from abstract, for the management issue has become a sore one, lately, for the AEC. The Commission's contract with the University of Chicago for the management of Argonne had been at issue in internecine conflicts that rent the scientific and academic community and produced forceful representations to President Johnson and his science adviser, Jerome Wiesner, by a large corps of Midwest congressmen who protested that their region had not received a fair share of federal funds for university research.[8] When, in January 1964, President Johnson rejected the proposal of the Midwest Universities Research Association that an accelerator estimated to cost $170 million be constructed at Madison, in part because "I found it impossible to justify starting another national laboratory close by [Argonne]," he added:

I would hope and expect that the fine staff of MURA will be able to continue to serve the Midwest through the universities and at Argonne, and I have asked Glenn Seaborg to use his good offices in that direction. I have also asked him to take all possible steps to make possible an increase in the participation of the academic institutions of the Midwest in the work of the Argonne Laboratory.[9]

The unusual plan for the management of Argonne announced by the AEC in October 1964 aimed to fulfill that promise. (It was still in the aiming stage in May 1966, and the contract establishing the new management arrangements finally went into effect on Nov. 1, 1966.) It called for a tripartite agreement between the AEC, the University of Chicago, and a new nonprofit corporation of midwest universities which "will formulate the Laboratory's policies and programs" while Chicago "will continue to operate the Labora-

[8] If "fair share" is defined as expenditures proportionate to the number of science doctorates awarded, a measure the National Science Foundation has used upon appropriate occasions, they were undoubtedly right. In statistics appended to President Johnson's January 16, 1964, letter to Senator Hubert Humphrey to support the proposition that "this area [the Midwest] has been treated with fairness," the measure of population was used, and expenditures at government-owned university-operated laboratories were excluded for all agencies but the AEC. Even these politic statistics supported the President's case in only 3 of 22 entries. See *AEC Authorizing Legislation Fiscal Year 1965*, Hearings before the Joint Committee on Atomic Energy, 88 Cong. 2 sess. (1964), Pt. 3, pp. 1480-81.

[9] From Jan. 16, 1964 letter of President Johnson to Senator Hubert Humphrey, *ibid.*, p. 1480.

tory responsive to the policies of the corporation. . . ."[10] It remains to be seen whether such an elaborate arrangement among formerly discordant powers will prove viable in the administration of a laboratory with major missions of reactor development as well as of basic research. The Founders Agreement of the new corporation, the Argonne Universities Association, contains a protective clause inserted at the AEC's request that "the Corporation and the University of Chicago will have the responsibility to comply with applicable laws, orders and regulations and to assure that the Laboratory will continue to function in accordance with overall policies and requirements of the Atomic Energy Commission"; but the possibilities of disagreement are not reduced by the multiplication of parties to an alliance. Much will depend upon the wisdom and restraint of key AUA and Chicago staff. If they can develop a concerted program that recognizes AEC's programmatic needs and budgetary realities, Argonne may gain new technical and political strength; if they cannot—perhaps it is kindest not to speculate.

Across the country at Palo Alto, a good deal of controversy has been generated over several issues in the management of the $114 million Stanford linear accelerator. A conflict-of-interest problem led to the resignation of one of the two joint directors and the exclusion of the most highly qualified firm from bidding on a key machine component; some heat was generated over the university's insistence on handling the subcontracting for the machine's construction, which many AEC staff wanted to do themselves (nonetheless, construction has set an enviable record of maintaining both time and budget schedules); and friction between the university's physics department and the accelerator center has not brightened the scene. Even the two California members of the Joint Committee on Atomic Energy, Chet Holifield and Craig Hosmer, reacted strongly to after-the-contract disclosures that the AEC was liable to a maximum annual rental of $375,000 should Stanford not be responsible for managing the facility or programming the experiments. ". . . those of us who supported this project so vigorously here are very disappointed," Hosmer observed, "and also promise that any attempt to get funds to

[10] AEC press release, Oct. 21, 1964.

pay rent to Stanford is going to meet with some very violent opposition."[11]

However, thoughtful and detailed arrangements have been worked out to ensure access to the Stanford instrument by qualified scientists from other institutions. And, though knowledgeable officials have asserted that multi-institutional management was precluded because the key man, Wolfgang Panofsky, was a Stanford professor and the facility was built on university land, the actual situation was more intricate. The original Stanford proposal of April 1957 suggested "that the Director of the project be responsible to a Board of Directors appointed by the President of Stanford University. It may be desirable to include on the Board representatives from neighboring academic institutions." The government responded with the suggestion that a "Brookhaven" style management might better guarantee that the facility would be available to scientists from other universities. Inquiries of sorts were thereupon made by Stanford physicists to three major west coast institutions inviting their opinion on what would constitute a desirable administrative arrangement; the replies confirmed them in their resolve to proceed along the lines of their original proposal.

In an attempt to forestall discord and rivalry over the management of the prospective 200-bev accelerator comparable to that manifested in the process of determining its site, the Commission has encouraged the formation of a national entente of major universities, the Universities Research Association, Inc. (URAI). The Association, a District of Columbia corporation headquartered initially in the National Academy of Sciences' building, was formally established in June 1965 by the presidents of thirty-four universities, each of which pledged $100,000 that may be drawn upon to meet expenses not reimbursable under government contracts (although such costs are normally covered by the management allowance). The presidents themselves would meet perhaps once a year, delegating the formulation of accelerator policies to an elected board (including one trustee from each of fifteen regional groupings of two to three constituent institutions and six

---

[11] *AEC Authorizing Legislation Fiscal Year 1963*, Hearings before the Subcommittee on Legislation of the Joint Committee on Atomic Energy, 87 Cong. 2 sess. (April and May 1962), p. 240.

trustees-at-large representing the public interest) of eminent physicists, scientists, and/or administrators, who

. . . should from the start adopt the view that they represent the interests of the association and the laboratory and not their home institutions. They should serve for sufficiently long periods of time and
convene sufficiently often to become fully conversant with the problems of the association and its facilities. . . . Generally speaking, the
scientific quality of the proposed experiments would be the primary
basis for determining access to the machine and associated facilities.
Visitors from institutions not in the association would be entitled to
the same privileges as those from member institutions.[12]

Just who took the initiative in launching the association, the
Commission or the National Academy of Sciences, was unclear;
privately, some witnesses said it had been the Academy, but Seaborg suggested "it was a matter of mutual recognition. . . ."[13] Nor
were the grounds for inviting particular university presidents
specified. One president who attended the founding session in
January 1965 stated, "It was the unanimous agreement that . . .
any university with an interest in high-energy physics should be
invited to join," but he added, "To make sure that all regions of
the country were represented, some universities whose high-energy physics activities are not yet fully developed are also included."[14] An initial limit "in the vicinity of 30" was set as "near
the maximum that would be manageable";[15] It will be interesting
to see if pressures to enlarge that number can be resisted. The
principal academic sector not represented in URAI to date is the
independent liberal arts college. Beyond that, the exclusion of
other sectors of society was forcefully noted by Craig Hosmer, the
senior Republican Congressman on the Joint Committee:

. . . this University Research Associates, Inc., [sic] . . . have voluntar-
ily banded themselves together to include a large portion of prestige
seeking university presidents, more or less an "in" group who desire to

[12] From a "Summary of Conclusions" of the founding meeting of university presidents held Jan. 17, 1965 at the National Academy of Sciences at the invitation of
Academy President Frederick Seitz. See *High Energy Physics Research*, Hearings before the Subcommittee on Research, Development and Radiation of the Joint Committee on Atomic Energy, 89 Cong. 1 sess. (March 2-5, 1965), pp. 8-9.
[13] See the discussion between Joint Committee members and Chairman Seaborg in
High Energy Physics Research, op. cit., p. 6.
[14] Letter to the writer, Aug. 25, 1965.
[15] "Summary of Conclusions," *High Energy Physics Research*, p. 8,

capture this 200 Bev . . . some people seriously feel that that kind of organization excludes necessary inputs from other segments of the culture of our country, political and otherwise and it is not exactly the kind of organization that they would want to see this facility placed under.

. . . it certainly appears to me that some reformation will have to be made in URAI. It is needed high in the organization by way of adding to the . . . board of directors . . . representatives of the public and perhaps even at least a representative of the Joint Committee staff, possibly the AEC itself, because once these people get behind a wall and only come out and only talk their own sort of language these things get far beyond public control.[16]

There is a visible danger throughout the system of government financed research at universities that the indispensable principle of equitable treatment to all applicants will gradually be transformed into the politically attractive principle of "something for all." As the urgency and secrecy of much AEC research at universities abates and its basic research programs expand, this danger is likely to grow. Not the least attractive feature of compacts of universities, as some laboratory directors are keenly aware, is the increased number of congressmen whom they can bring into sympathetic acquaintance with the national laboratory in their midst.

With the foregoing reservations, we will nevertheless try to summarize the conclusions that may be drawn from the government, and especially the AEC, postwar experience about conditions under which multi-university management of a research facility should be seriously considered. By management we mean the assignment of significant responsibility for major laboratory policies to the president and trustees of more than one university, commonly exercised by one or more authorized university representatives who function not in an advisory capacity but in a line authority over the laboratory director. *Management* should be distinguished from *utilization*, a related matter to be discussed shortly.

The strictly educational functions of inter-university associations do not normally require their assumption of responsibility for managing a laboratory. Such functions include working out

---

[16] See *AEC Authorizing Legislation Fiscal Year 1967*, Hearings before the Joint Committee on Atomic Energy, 1966, Pt. 3, p. 1326.

and facilitating the terms under which faculty and graduate students are selected and given leave and funds to undertake research at a government installation; helping to improve courses and research in nuclear fields at member institutions; and, in general, acting as an educational intermediary between the laboratory and universities in the region. They have been well served by the Oak Ridge Institute of Nuclear Studies (ORINS) and, to a lesser degree, the Associated Midwest Universities (AMU) and, to a still lesser degree, similar but smaller and less active associations emerging in the orbit of the Hanford, Los Alamos, and other laboratories. However, ORINS, which has a modest research program of its own, has at times aspired to manage the Oak Ridge National Laboratory; and a group of universities akin to AMU exercised significant policy responsibilities in the early days at Argonne.[17]

[17] After the University of Chicago withdrew from the management of the Oak Ridge laboratory in 1945, it was succeeded for a brief period by Monsanto. When Monsanto prepared to relinquish the contract, the AEC at first invited Chicago to return. Southern universities having been less than overjoyed at the invasion of their territory by a northern institution, the Oak Ridge Institute of Nuclear Studies thereupon offered to manage the laboratory. However, for a variety of reasons, the contract went not to Chicago but to Union Carbide. Following the change of contractors at Hanford in 1965 and the contemplated change at Argonne, membership in ORINS was expanded, and the corporation was retitled Oak Ridge Associated Universities. Some members hoped that another bid (or invitation) to manage the Oak Ridge laboratory would result, but, at least in 1965, this was evidently not the corporation's intent.

Plans for the management of the Argonne National Laboratory were originally drafted by a committee of Midwest university delegates appointed in December 1945 by General Leslie Groves and Colonel Kenneth Nichols. Under these plans, which went into effect in 1946, the laboratory had an advisory Board of Governors consisting of seven scientists (elected, in turn, by a council composed of representatives of 29 Midwest institutions) which "reviews the research programs and operating budgets presented by the [laboratory] Director and must approve them before they are submitted by the contractor [the University of Chicago] to the government." See Farrington Daniels, first chairman of the Board, "The Argonne National Laboratory," *Bulletin of the Atomic Scientists* (June 1948), pp. 177-78.

It would be interesting to know more about how this board actually functioned, and when and why it was discontinued, particularly as the AEC is now reconstituting a similar arrangement for the management of Argonne. One informant indicated that the Army's hope to establish a "Brookhaven" style of management was frustrated by the distrust and conflict that developed between Chicago and other Midwest universities. The Commission's assignment to Argonne, in 1948, of heavy responsibility for R&D on naval nuclear reactors also played an important part in the universities' withdrawal, since this classified work changed the complexion of the laboratory that had previously been devoted primarily to basic research. Even during the brief period the

The positive virtues of giving the management of a laboratory to a group of universities are that the laboratory can draw more readily upon a larger pool of men, resources, advice, and good will; the negative virtues are that such management can more readily escape the conflicts between rival universities and between scientists and administrators of a single university (for example, over the division of the government overhead and fee—an issue in which AEC officers have been embroiled, try as they may to escape it), and avoids conferring the tangible and intangible benefits of a large installation upon only one of several worthy institutions. The insulation from academic politics has weighed heavily in the thinking of several AEC officials who favor multi-university management for basic research laboratories located off campus; and the original proposal for four national laboratories advanced to General Groves in 1946 by an advisory committee of seven leading scientists recommended that a number of institutions be represented on the board of directors of each laboratory.[18]

The drawback of such an arrangement is directly proportionate to the amount of authority retained by the multi-university board and inversely proportional to the magnitude, urgency, and complexity of the laboratory's work. Thus, to cite an extreme case, an institute for advanced research in pure mathematics, composed of individual scholars working alone and at their own pace on problems of their own choosing, should encounter few difficulties and many advantages governed by a group of universities. But a (basic or applied) research laboratory with massive and expensive equipment operated and maintained by a large staff of scientists, engineers, technicians, laborers, and clerical and administrative personnel cannot function effectively without clear lines of responsibility running to a director vested with sufficient authority to make instant decisions (on which large sums and the success of major experiments may hinge) to operate an instrument or shut it down for repair, to transfer supporting personnel from one department to another, and to assign or reassign priorities among competing programs for access to various facilities and services.

Board of Governors functioned, the laboratory budget grew so much that, it was said, the Board could not review it in detail.

[18] Hewlett and Anderson, op. cit., p. 634. According to one informant, the proposal was actually included in Groves's original charge to the committee.

According to this line of reasoning, the National Science Foundation's research facilities have functioned well because their operating costs have been relatively low and, in any event, they have been devoted to pure research in which there is no ready measure of efficiency or, for long periods, of success and an easy hand on the reins (or many hands on many reins) is not only tolerable but desirable. Furthermore, the Foundation has the subsidiary objective of raising the quality of scientific research and education at lesser universities, which is advanced by the association of eminent and not so eminent universities on the same governing board; whereas, despite their significant contributions to pure science and scientific education, AEC laboratories must ever remain alert to possible military and industrial applications of their findings, and to comparisons of their efficiency with laboratories operated by industry. Finally, of both the NSF and the AEC centers, it is said that success hinges more on the character of the director than on the nature of the contracting organization. The success of a laboratory depends on its day-to-day management; "the Board is useful only when things go wrong."

A careful comparison of the administrative and scientific performance of the two largest AEC "pure" research laboratories, at Berkeley and Brookhaven, would be revealing, as each has done outstanding work under a different system of management. Initially, General Groves had felt that Brookhaven demanded a degree of freedom that was incompatible with the responsibilities of a government agency to account for public funds and to promote an objective recognizably like one sanctioned by the Congress. Unlike the University of California, whose officers had acquired enough experience during the war years to draw an acceptable line—or, rather, to accept the line drawn by events—between their own and the government's programmatic and budgetary responsibilities, "Some of the AUI trustees . . . held out for little or no control. Groves did not believe the federal authorities should pass on detailed laboratory experiments, but he argued that public officials could not abdicate their duty to exercise ultimate approval of research programs, budgets, general administrative practices, wages, and salaries."[19] Since that day both managements have moved toward more common ground, California gaining a degree

[19] *Ibid.*, p. 637.

of freedom and initiative it lacked during the war, while AUI has learned to live with the government and to delegate more authority to its laboratory director. Indeed, in the eyes of some AEC staff, AUI has developed from an inexperienced and difficult to a sophisticated and efficient contractor, qualified in administration, construction, and engineering as well as in physics.[20] Two employees independently ascribed AUI's success to the fact that board members were mature men with wide experience in science and in the administration and politics of science, who did not act as "representatives" of their institutions, and put great trust and authority in their laboratory directors:

This type of arrangement prevents the nepotic type interference which direct management by many or single universities can produce. As a result, the Brookhaven Director does not have to withstand direct pressure from a single university through the Board of Trustees for favored treatment, and participation in the scientific programs does not involve favoritism to scientists of AUI universities. Other factors instrumental in determining the healthy status of research operations in Brookhaven are the limited size of its Board of Trustees, which has been carefully preserved . . . , as well as delegation to the Director of the Laboratory of sufficient freedom to assure effective management.[21]

The record of Berkeley and Brookhaven shows that either one or a group of universities can successfully manage a large research laboratory—or run into trouble doing so; and it may well be that the chances of trouble are somewhat greater at least in the earlier stages of management by a group of universities. However, there are in this nation at least a dozen universities and institutes of technology of high quality whose senior faculty and administrators have now had two decades of experience in managing major government research enterprises, and dozens more of somewhat lesser

[20] To judge from the observations of a senior AEC official in the course of a private interview in 1955, the turning point in university management came some time around 1954: "Several years ago, even two years ago, I would have had considerable doubt about the ability of universities, or groups of universities, to operate establishments like our national laboratories. In the last year or so the university-run outfits have improved tremendously. They have learned a lesson: big laboratories cannot be run like a university. For example, in the early days of Brookhaven, the Board insisted on reviewing every salary above $3,000. This was unadulterated hogwash and they came to recognize it as such." Whether a blaze of insight suddenly enveloped these contractors in 1954 or things simply tend to improve shortly before the time that an interviewer goes around looking for trouble is a point on which we need not dwell.

[21] Letter, July 1965.

quality and experience. The purer the research, the more unique the facility, and the greater its (primary or secondary) educational function, the stronger is the logic for multi-institutional management. The more programmatic the research and the more closely it must be meshed with other agency activities, the stronger is the case for management by a single, responsible, and responsive institution. (One laboratory administrator, deeply disturbed at news that a group of universities might replace Chicago at Argonne, felt that this would render Argonne less responsive to AEC needs in the area of reactor development and foster a conflict between the interests of university scientists in pure research and the Commission's responsibilities to promote specific kinds of practical research on a specific schedule, coordinating the work of Argonne with that of other government and industry laboratories.)

Where conditions lead the AEC, nonetheless, to contract with a single university for the operation of a unique basic research facility, it has a responsibility to ensure that access to the facility is determined by the quality of the experiments proposed rather than by the institutional affiliation of the scientists proposing them.

Allocating Machine Time

The enormous cost of large particle accelerators, rendering each machine unique for certain experimental purposes, has created a demand for machine time that cannot be fully satisfied despite the multiplication of experimental stations at the target areas. National laboratories have, therefore, had to face the problem of allocating machine time among claimants from their resident staff and scientists at institutions throughout the nation and the world. The problem promises to grow more acute and merits continued study both by those responsible for the management of these machines and by the scientists seeking to use them. The views of the former group were reflected in the Ramsey report of April 1963 and of the latter, in the comments on this report prepared shortly thereafter by members of the Good panel.[22]

[22] A committee of eminent physicists chaired by Norman Ramsey of Harvard was convened in November 1962 by the President's Science Advisory Committee and the AEC General Advisory Committee "to assess the future needs in the fields of high energy accelerator physics." Their report, published by the AEC in May 1963, is reproduced in *AEC Authorizing Legislation Fiscal Year 1965*, Hearings before the Joint

Both reports were in fundamental accord and, where they disagreed, greater weight must, in general, be attached to the conclusions of the Ramsey panel because of the eminence and experience of its members and the more thorough nature of their study. Both reports agreed that "essentially all new accelerators . . . should be available to competent scientists and groups of scientists without regard to their current affiliations but rather in accordance with the scientific merit of their proposals."[23] The Ramsey report suggested that "For the very large laboratories, a figure of at least one-half outside research participation may be an appropriate starting point for planning. . . ."[24] The Good panel offered no figure, stating merely that "the on-site group should not dominate the program" and adding the significant observation that users need not only time scheduled in advance but more quickly arranged "informal access to some small fraction of machine output. . . ."

While both reports recognized the need for further study of the scientific implications of different managerial arrangements, the Good panel recommended that "outside groups should have a voice *and responsibility* [our italics] in certain [unspecified] aspects of laboratory management" and declared that the laboratory director should "be responsible to a governing body of wide national representation." The Ramsey panel refrained from assigning such management responsibility to a group of scientists, confining itself to the observation that "there must be national representation on the committee or board which determines the policies of use. Such a scientific policy committee can deal with the danger of overwhelming advantage being extended to permanent on-site workers or to the staff of the university or group of universities holding the operating contract for the facility."[25] This type

---

Committee on Atomic Energy, Pt. 3, pp. 1689-751, from which our references are taken. In the course of evaluating the Ramsey report, the Office of Science and Technology took the commendable step of asking a group of young physicists chaired by Dr. Myron Good of the University of Wisconsin "to see how they felt about the [Ramsey panel] recommendations." (*Ibid.*, p. 1478.) As this group could not reach agreement in the short time available, no single report was prepared; each member simply wrote a letter setting forth his views. A summary of these letters (evidently prepared by OST staff), appearing as Attachment C in the foregoing hearings, pp. 1506-07, is the source of our citations.

[23] Ramsey report, *op. cit.*, p. 1706.

[24] *Ibid.*, p. 1707.

[25] *Idem.*

of arrangement would be compatible with that worked out for the Stanford Linear Accelerator, where a Scientific Policy Committee of ten scientists (two from Stanford and eight from other institutions) nominated by Stanford and approved by the AEC serves in an advisory capacity to the president of Stanford, but has no line responsibility between the AEC and its contractor, Stanford, or between the contractor (as represented by the Stanford board of trustees or president) and the laboratory director.

Information on the proportion of the operating time of various accelerators taken by visiting scientists (Table 7) suggests that managerial arrangements influence the net outcome (which is not to assert that other factors do *not*). Plans for the Stanford accelerator aim for 50 percent usage by visiting scientists, and for the behemoth 200-bev "about 70%."[26] At the National Science Foundation's optical and radio telescope observatories (at Kitt Peak, Ariz., and Green Bank, W.Va., respectively), managed by incorporated groups of universities, some 60-70 percent of the time on major instruments has been utilized by outside scientists, whereas a 50:50 split between outside and resident staff time has been planned for the NSF Owens Valley radio telescope managed by the California Institute of Technology and the high energy accelerator managed by Cornell University.

Altogether, the experience of both the AEC and the NSF suggests that the management of a basic research facility by a single university is more likely to lead to heavier use by resident scientists than is management by a group of universities. This view is disputed by advocates of single university management, who argue that access is determined by policy and programming committees of scientists, which function independently of the mode of management. Nonetheless, we believe that a larger look at the facts bears it out. Management need not determine the pattern of ma-

---

[26] From a paper "Proposed New National Accelerator Laboratory for Research in High Energy Physics" distributed by the AEC in 1965 to those interested in submitting a site proposal for the machine. "Sixty or seventy percent, or more" was the outside use envisaged by AEC Chairman Seaborg and "about 75 percent" by the National Academy of Sciences' committee which evaluated sites. See *Impact of Federal Research and Development Policies on Scientific and Technical Manpower,* Hearings before the Subcommittee on Employment and Manpower of the Senate Labor and Public Welfare Committee, 89 Cong. 1 sess. (1965), p. 621, and *Congressional Record* (March 22, 1966), daily ed., p. 6245.

TABLE 7

Use of AEC Accelerators by Visiting Scientists, 1964[a]

Site	Percent of research time taken by outside users	Approximate Number of Outside		
		Universities[b]	Ph.D. scientists[c]	Graduate students[c]
Argonne[d]	*80*	13	85	60
Brookhaven[e]	*65*	37	260	200
Berkeley[f]	*35*	13	87	72
Cambridge	*35*	8	64	59
Princeton-Penn.	*20*	6	56	61

Source: *High Energy Physics Research*, Hearings before the Subcommittee on Research, Development, and Radiation of the Joint Committee on Atomic Energy, 89 Cong. 1 sess. (March 1965), p. 378. Notes d, e, f from other sources.

[a] Calendar year 1964.

[b] Not additive, as some universities were represented at several facilities.

[c] Refers only to those performing experiments during the year, and not to those analyzing data from past, or preparing for future, experiments. A few visiting more than one laboratory may be entered more than once.

[d] Partial operation of the Argonne synchrotron started in early 1964. During that year, about 80 percent of machine time was taken by outside users; the laboratory sought to strengthen its staff to the point where they might take first 30, and ultimately 50, percent, but made little progress because of budgetary restrictions.

[e] Includes both the AGS and the Cosmotron; at the latter, visitors used about 70% of the operating time.

[f] The time taken by visitors has evidently been rising in recent years; in June 1964, we were given an estimate of 30 percent outside use, and a figure of about 15 percent (one-seventh of the time) has been reported for an earlier period (see Warren Hagstrom, *Social Control in Modern Science*, Ph.D. thesis, University of California, Berkeley, 1963, p. 270).

chine use and, indeed, can do little about it at any particular moment in time. But, over a span of years, it can (with the government's concurrence and financial support), strengthen the number and quality of resident staff, or restrict their growth to the minimum required for a viable installation existing primarily to serve visiting scientists. By and large, basic research facilities managed by a compact of universities have preferred, or for other reasons accepted, the latter role; whereas those managed by a single university (selected because of its distinction in that field of science) have more readily pursued the former.

Of course, the optimal use pattern for a particular machine depends upon the institutional distribution of scientists qualified to use it; but the policies of the government and of the operating contractor have a pronounced effect on the number and competence of staff attached to a facility. If a university permits salary splitting by tenured faculty conducting research at a national laboratory (e.g., permits a professor to draw a third of his academic year salary from the laboratory budget for devoting a third of his time to research at the laboratory), the university department can be correspondingly enlarged and the lure of a faculty appointment at a leading university can help the laboratory attract a first-class staff. Approximately this situation has prevailed at Berkeley, producing a large physics department and a correspondingly high degree of machine use by resident staff.[27] At Argonne, however, where one observer remarked "they are having a devil of a time getting capable research staff," relatively greater participation by visiting scientists is necessary for adequate machine utilization. The prospects for attracting an eminent permanent staff to the Stanford accelerator have not been enhanced by the unfortunate cleavage between departmental and laboratory physicists.

Several physicists suggested that the principal function of user groups is less practical than personal or political: a similar allocation of machine time was likely to eventuate in any case, but "it means a lot to all the users, and there are good psychological reasons for it." Thus, one noted, part of the drive for an independent accelerator by physicists associated with the Midwest Universities Research Association and for the subsequent move to broaden the control of Argonne stemmed from a feeling that access to the Argonne accelerator could be cut off "at the whim" of the University of Chicago. Outside physicists had been asked to advise on the use of the Argonne machine and, they conceded, their advice *had,* in fact, been taken; nonetheless, they felt, Chicago was under no "compulsion" to take it.

Advocating a 50:50 allocation of machine time between resident and visiting scientists, a perceptive physicist advanced the argument paraphrased in the following paragraph:

Visiting scientists want to control the use of an accelerator, but do not care to invest the amount of time necessary to design it or to make the many mundane but important engineering decisions involved in its construction and operation. The theoretical physicist identifies the need for a particular machine and experiment,

[27] Even close outside observers believe that the amount of salary splitting by Berkeley physicists and chemists is far more extensive than has, in fact, been the case; it has been only a contributing factor in the growth of these departments which were eminent before the government research boom began.

and eventually gets credit for it; but the experimentalist and the engineer have to build the machine and set up the experiment. It is hard to get a bright young high energy physicist to devote himself for several years to the construction of a machine, since that is not the best way for him to advance his reputation. However, the ultimate effectiveness of the machine rests on a real rapport between its builders and users. Both Brookhaven and Berkeley have established a mutual respect between the engineers and scientists—and this is not an easy thing to do. It is not the rule in industry, where the engineer, typically, asks for the design and says to the scientists, "You go away and come back when it is built."[28] One reason we have been more successful in high energy physics than the Russians is because of the greater cooperation we have achieved between scientists and engineers. If a Russian scientist wants a magnet, he sends his request to the government, which issues an order—and when the magnet is delivered it doesn't work, because there has been no communication between the builders and users during the process of production.

Clearly, it lies within the government's power, by budgeting larger or smaller funds to a laboratory or to outside scientists, to influence the use which is made of a facility. We believe that power should be used, in part, to encourage the residence of a core group of first-class physicists in each major region of the country (i.e., the minimum number required to keep the field alive: to conduct a first-class doctoral program); but primarily to ensure that the research conducted at the laboratory is of the highest possible quality, variety, and originality. The allocation of machine time between laboratory and visiting scientists (and between professors and graduate students!) at any particular facility should be that which best advances these goals.[29]

[28] This is quite untrue of any industry like electronics or chemical engineering, one reader comments. "There is not a single new chemical process in which the scientist is not involved in the whole process; the scientist gets shoved aside only when . . . [he] wants to change the entire design every day or to make suggestions about things . . . [he doesn't] know anything about."

[29] "But who determines the allocation?" asks a reader. The answer "those scientifically best qualified to do so" may be too general. Translated into administrative terms, it would require representation on a screening committee of the major reputable scientific factions and interests seeking access (including graduate students), and the designation as director of a scientist of great standing and breadth of outlook.

CHAPTER V

The "Multi-Program" Laboratories

Special attention must be given to the group of AEC laboratories variously known as "national" and/or "multi-purpose" or "multi-program" laboratories. Strictly speaking, there are only three "national" laboratories in the AEC complex—the Brookhaven National Laboratory, the Argonne National Laboratory, and the Oak Ridge National Laboratory. In addition to these, the AEC has characterized the following as "multi-program" laboratories: the Ames Laboratory, the Lawrence Radiation Laboratory at Berkeley and Livermore, and the Los Alamos Scientific Laboratory.[1] Due to the lesser scale and scope of its programs, Ames will not be considered further here (see Table 8). It is interesting to note that the directors of the foregoing laboratories have had enough in common to meet together informally once a year to discuss matters of common interest;[2] senior professional and administrative staff,

[1] See *The Future Role of the Atomic Energy Commission Laboratories,* Joint Committee on Atomic Energy, 86 Cong. 2 sess. (1960), p. 9.

[2] This "laboratory directors club," as one member called it, was apparently initiated by Leland Haworth while he was director of Brookhaven; it was discontinued upon his departure and reconstituted at the initiative of Alvin Weinberg, director of the Oak Ridge laboratory. Another member, who attached so little importance to the group that he had some difficulty identifying it, suggested that participants had most of the following points in common: all reported to Spofford English, Assistant General Manager for Research and Development; were old-timers in the business, having been in the research phase of the Manhattan District; had been involved in the postwar declassification work of Richard Tolman; and were connected with laboratories which

TABLE 8

R&D Expenditures and Missions of Multi-Program Laboratories, FY 1964

(In millions of dollars)

Program	Total	Laboratory Expenditures						
		Oak Ridge	Argonne	Brookhaven	Los Alamos	Berkeley	Livermore	Ames
Physical research	$121.8	$25.7	$27.8	$27.9	$ 1.8	$29.4	$ 4.1	$5.1
Reactor development	111.5	31.2	27.3	5.3	35.1	0.1	11.4	1.1
Biology and medicine	26.8	8.6	5.9	6.2	1.1	3.2	1.8	—
Other[b]	12.2	4.7	0.1	1.2	—	—	6.2	—
Total	$272.3	$70.2	$61.1	$40.6	$38.0[a]	$32.7	$23.5[a]	$6.2
Character of Mission[c]								
Physical sciences and engineering								
Basic research		x	x	x	x	x	x	x
Applied research and general								
development		x	x	x	x		x	x
Project development		x	x	x	x		x	
Biological and medical research		x	x	x	x	x	x	

[a] R&D weapons expenditures are excluded from this table, reducing the total volume of R&D at Los Alamos and Livermore. Total FY 1964 operating costs at Los Alamos were $85.4 million and at Livermore, $107 million. *Sources:* AEC and *Impact of Federal Research and Development Policies on Scientific and Technical Manpower,* Hearings before the Subcommittee on Employment and Manpower of the Senate Labor and Public Welfare Committee, 89 Cong. 1 sess. 1965), p. 605.

[b] Includes isotopes development and civilian applications of nuclear explosives (at Livermore) but not training, education, and information.

[c] *The Future Role of the Atomic Energy Commission Laboratories,* Joint Committee on Atomic Energy, 1960, p. 10, with the addition of an entry for biological research at Livermore. This report provides the following definitions (p. 7):

"*Basic research . . .* is research where the primary aim of the investigator is a fuller knowledge or understanding of the subject under study rather than a practical application."

"*Applied research and general development* categorizes work undertaken or carried out because of the clear probability that it will have a useful end result. It is applied to work of a general nature as distinguished from a specific development project."

"*Project development* includes all effort devoted to the solution of specific problems encountered in producing an end product. . . ."

such as the chairmen of physics departments, business managers, budget officers, and fiscal officers, among others, also confer periodically. All of these laboratories, but Oak Ridge, are managed by universities or an incorporated group of universities, and while a great deal might be said about Oak Ridge, it would all add up to the fact that this is a pretty special laboratory.[3] The general budgetary standing of the "multi-program" laboratories among other major AEC laboratories, is indicated in Table 9.

The AEC has characterized the "multi-program" laboratories as "integrated" or "balanced" facilities, meaning thereby, evidently, that they have a broad range of scientific and technical competence and conduct basic research in the physical and biological sciences as well as applied research and technical development in some fields of nuclear technology. "The multi-disciplinary nature of the National Laboratories . . . is what is really meant by 'balance' . . . ," one laboratory official suggests. "What I am referring to is not only the free and easy interaction between scientists of various disciplines, but a spirit of operation which takes such interaction for granted and actively encourages it." Of course, the degree of "balance" varies considerably; the concentration of Berkeley on pure physics has been balanced by Livermore's emphasis on applied work in ramjet and rocket propulsion, weaponry, and the civilian use of nuclear explosives. Various AEC staff estimated in 1963 and 1964 that basic research constituted perhaps 20-30 percent of the work at Oak Ridge, 50 percent of that at Argonne, and 80 percent or more of that at Brookhaven. By "balance," the AEC seems to mean *some* (not necessarily much) participation in

did a large volume of basic research. One laboratory director who had sought to attend a meeting and not been invited felt that some scientific stigma was attached to the refusal: that his laboratory was not recognized as doing enough basic research to qualify. Members were aware not only of their similar but their conflicting interests, such as who would get the nod from the AEC and the Joint Committee for a new machine or program.

[3] Among the atypical features of Oak Ridge, as an industrially managed laboratory, are: the exceptional amount of decentralized authority vested in it by Union Carbide; the broad interests of its director, Alvin Weinberg, and, following in part from them, the unusually broad scope of its mission; the special position and strength of the AEC Oak Ridge office, site of the Manhattan District headquarters; and, perhaps, its association with the Oak Ridge Institute of Nuclear Studies, the strongest educational combine of universities in the AEC enclave.

TABLE 9

Budget, Plant, Employment, and Inception of Major AEC Laboratories, 1964

(Dollar amounts in millions)

Laboratory	Operating cost[a]	Cost of plant[b]	Employ-ment[b]	Date started[c]	Notes
Sandia	$213.6	$153.1	8,218	Sept. 1945	Established as extension of Los Alamos; management transferred to Sandia Corp. Nov. 1949.
*Livermore[d]	107.0	148.3	5,735	March 1950	Set up as weapons laboratory July 1952.
*Los Alamos	85.4	200.2	4,211	April 1943	
*Oak Ridge	70.7	211.2	4,980	March 1948	Predecessor, Clinton Laboratories, established 1943.
Bettis	66.2	118.3	2,905	Dec. 1948	
*Argonne	62.1	232.8	5,494	July 1946	Predecessor, Metallurgical Laboratory, established 1942.
Atomics International	61.8	35.9[e]	3,496	May 1948	First contract with North American.
Knolls	48.7	120.5	2,131	May 1946	First contract with General Electric.
*Brookhaven	40.7	162.9	3,326	March 1947	Site transferred to AEC.
*Berkeley[d]	32.6	78.5	3,226	May 1943	Manhattan District assumed support of Radiation Laboratory, established 1939.
Hanford	31.6	92.2	1,828	1943	

Source: *Impact of Federal Research and Development Policies on Scientific and Technical Manpower*, Hearings before the Subcommittee on Employment and Manpower of the Senate Labor and Public Welfare Committee, 89 Cong. 1 sess. (1965), p. 605.

* "Multi-program" laboratories.

a Fiscal year 1964.

b As of June 30, 1964.

c Approximate. It will be noted that the dates given here for some laboratories (for example, Los Alamos, Brookhaven, and Sandia) vary somewhat from those in Table 4.

d Together comprise E. O. Lawrence Radiation Laboratory, embraced under a single contract with the University of California.

e AEC funds only; AI has invested another $25 million.

two or more broad R&D program areas embraced administratively by the Divisions of Research, Biology and Medicine, Reactor Development, Military Application, and Production. But more important, "balance" seems to signify an intention to insulate these laboratories from abrupt and radical changes—especially cutbacks —in their budgets, and to lend them a special degree of stability or, at least, to manifest a special concern about the effect that a major cut in one program may have on other programs at the laboratory, and on overall laboratory overhead and support functions.

As in any dynamic organization, this balance [in the programs of multi-program laboratories] is continually shifting. . . . Continuity, however, must be maintained if the intellectual vigor and productivity of the organization is to be preserved. . . . Discontinuities in this balance caused by the sudden elimination or the drastic curtailment of a single activity can have serious effects on apparently remote programs since frequently the value of a staff group is not confined to the activity which provides its principal support. In the case of these multi-program laboratories, therefore, the Commission is faced with a peculiarly sensitive and complex management problem. . . .[4]

This profusion of words conveys a feeling better than a meaning. The feeling is that the future of the multi-program laboratories is somehow more assured and more closely linked to that of the AEC than is that of most of the other government-owned, contractor-operated laboratories designated variously as "project engineering laboratories," "production plant laboratories," or "university laboratories," with narrower, if important, functions.[5] It is the multi-purpose laboratories that, as AEC Chairman Glenn Seaborg has

---

[4] *The Future Role of the Atomic Energy Commission Laboratories, op. cit.,* p. 9.

[5] Thus, the industry-operated "project engineering laboratories"—Sandia, Knolls, Bettis, the General Electric laboratory at Evendale, and the Pratt-Whitney facility at Middletown (closed out in 1965)—have had the task of developing nuclear weapons, naval reactors, aircraft propulsion reactors, or SNAP devices for the nuclear generation of auxiliary electric power, all classified operations largely for military purposes and involving little basic research; the "production plant laboratories" at Hanford and Savannah River have been responsible for assisting and improving the production of special nuclear materials; and the "university laboratories"—the Argonne Cancer Research Hospital, the Cambridge and Princeton accelerators, the Princeton stellerator—for research in designated areas (*ibid.,* pp. 8-13).

stated, "serve, for many purposes, in a capacity similar to GOGO (government-owned, government-operated) laboratories."[6]

The Commission has ascribed six functions to these laboratories as a group (not necessarily to each laboratory individually):

1. The conduct of "strong programs" of basic research.

2. Nuclear weapons development.

3. ". . . conceiving new devices for harnessing nuclear energy and new uses to which nuclear energy may be applied. . . . For any such items—whether conceived by these laboratories or assigned to them by the Commission . . .—it is appropriate for the investigations and developments of the laboratory to be carried through demonstration of technical feasibility and far enough to provide a basis for judging probable economic worth of the concept."

4. "From time to time, the Commission will utilize these laboratories and their staffs for other [i.e., non-nuclear] tasks or projects of importance to the Nation."

5. ". . . aiding the Commission in the rapid dissemination of new knowledge" by programs that go beyond "simply publishing the results of their own work," such as "on-the-job training for industrial personnel" or "cooperative programs with universities. . . ."

6. "Finally, the Commission will continue to obtain from these laboratories technical evaluations and advice."[7]

We will discuss each of these functions in turn except for number 4, the conduct of non-nuclear work, which poses such fundamental issues about the purpose not only of the laboratories, but of the AEC, that it seems preferable to leave this point to the last and consider it more fully.

Basic Research

Two kinds of basic research programs can be distinguished at AEC laboratories. There are those associated with or grafted onto a fundamentally practical mission, to help achieve it or simply to sharpen

[6] In making this remark, Seaborg cited all the multi-program laboratories (including Ames) and Sandia. See *Systems Development and Management,* Hearings before a Subcommittee of the House Government Operations Committee, 87 Cong. 2 sess. (1962), Pt. 5, p. 1644.

[7] *The Future Role of the Atomic Energy Commission Laboratories, op. cit.,* p. 12.

the intellectual edge of a laboratory. This has been, most notably, the kind conducted at Los Alamos and Livermore. Observers testify to the changeling nature of some eminent scientific minds who, bored with pure science, may become intrigued by applied work (classified work has a peculiar fascination of its own) and then, recoiling, seek again some yet unsullied truth. Viewed more mundanely by the Congress or a laboratory director:

> It is necessary for the continued health of a scientific laboratory to devote some of its efforts to pure research. This is of importance for many of the individuals who are at their best if they can participate to some extent in basic scientific work. It is also of importance for the standing of the Laboratory. Without significant publications, the Laboratory's reputation cannot be kept at a sufficiently high level and the Laboratory's ability of recruiting and keeping outstanding people will suffer. Finally, the cross fertilization between pure and applied scientific efforts cannot be overestimated.[8]

Programs of the second kind are those justified and budgeted explicitly in their own right. A prominent example is the research in particle physics at Brookhaven, Argonne, and Berkeley. This kind of research in the physical sciences is budgeted by the AEC Division of Research and, in the biological sciences, by the Division of Biology and Medicine, whereas the preceding kind may or may not be so budgeted—at the weapons laboratories, for example, it has been funded by the Division of Military Applications.

As basic research expenditures have risen, there has been increasing dispute about their appropriate volume and management. It was reported in July 1961 that Glenn Seaborg, first scientist to serve as Commission chairman, and his fellow scientist-commissioner Leland Haworth "want to see the level of physical research expenditures, currently at about $180-million annually, eventually equal that of the other major AEC programs, or about $500-million/yr" (a level projected by the Ramsey panel for high energy physics alone in 1973).[9] Basic research has been perhaps the

---

[8] From a September 1959 report of the Livermore laboratory, "Long Range Program Lawrence Radiation Laboratory—Livermore Site, 1959-69," in *The Future Role of the Atomic Energy Commission Laboratories, op. cit.,* p. 138.

[9] *Nucleonics* (July 1961), p. 26; and the Ramsey report, *op. cit.,* p. 1736. In FY 1962, the Division of Research budget was actually $172, not $180, million.

major realm of Commission activity about which the Joint Committee has periodically expressed skepticism. The continued rise of expenditures in this area, during a period when the total AEC budget has been leveling off, has not escaped the committee's critical attention, particularly in view of the termination, cutback, or postponement of a series of development programs favored by the committee, such as the aircraft nuclear propulsion program, the nuclear ramjet, nuclear merchant ships, the nuclear rocket, and a number of "SNAP" devices for nuclear-generated auxiliary power. ". . . we see a trend developing here," Committee Vice Chairman Chet Holifield admonished Seaborg in February 1964, "where basic research increases in funding and simultaneously development is beginning to be cut out. . . . If this trend is going to be a permanent factor some of us are going to lose a little bit of our enthusiasm for basic research."[10]

The Committee thereupon asked Donald Hornig, Director of the Office of Science and Technology, for a statement of national policy for high energy physics, and received in return a letter that one physicist characterized as a judicious compromise—"The Joint Committee felt it wasn't concrete enough; the scientific community felt it went too far in singling out one field of science" (for specific and expensive endorsement). In contrast to the Committee's linkage and comparison of expenditures for high energy physics with those for nuclear development, Hornig asserted that "The level and character of support for high-energy physics must be determined and periodically reassessed in the context of . . . the

---

[10] *AEC Authorizing Legislation Fiscal Year 1965, op. cit.,* Pt. 3, p. 1296. Some further remarks of Holifield on this occasion are worth noting: ". . . while research in the atomic energy program is up approximately 12 percent this year, expenditures for development are down approximately 3 percent. Similarly in the case of the Department of Defense, research expenditures are up about 1 percent while development is down more than 6 percent.

"This modest reduction in development expense is not our major concern—however, we are concerned that this may be the beginning of an unfortunate trend.

"Research is the broad road leading to improvements in technology, but development is a vital bridge that links the two. There is no 'payoff' from our research efforts either in terms of improved economic strength or national defense, unless the development bridge is completed. . . . It is our concern that the 'reorientation' of many AEC programs by eliminating their developmental objectives will lead to a situation on the floor of the House and in the Senate in which the broad road of research will run into funding difficulties" (*ibid.,* p. 1294).

overall national science program (rather than in relation to the applied research and development programs of the AEC) . . ."[11] This statement is of considerable interest, since it advanced a significant (if broad) new criterion for determining the appropriate level of basic research expenditures in a particular field: the model of a "national science program" that is more than a mere conglomeration of discrete agency programs. The Office of Science and Technology, the Bureau of the Budget, the National Science Foundation, the National Academy of Sciences, and several congressional committees have, in recent years, been collecting some of the information (on expenditures, personnel, facilities, and institutions in various fields of basic research) needed to set up this model. The ultimate effect of such a national program might well be to restrain somewhat the growth of expenditures for high energy physics, for, as a former AEC official is said to have observed after transferring to another agency, there are a lot of other needy and meritorious fields of science.

Some university spokesmen have complained that the small scale basic research projects of the mission-oriented laboratories

[11] From the March 27, 1964, letter of Hornig to Senator John Pastore, chairman of the Joint Committee on Atomic Energy, in *AEC Authorizing Legislation Fiscal Year 1965, op. cit.,* Pt. 3, p. 1511. This letter was essentially an interim reply to the committee's request for a statement of national policy, since it set no specific goals in terms of budgets or accelerators, although indicating the broad energy levels that future accelerators should reach. In effect, the committee asked the Administration to take a stand on the specific recommendations of the Ramsey report. ". . . the committee requests that the AEC, in conjunction with other appropriate federal agencies, prepare a study to be submitted to the President and the Congress on high energy physics research. . . . Pending the receipt and evaluation of this suggested study, it will be difficult to justify levels of funding for high energy physics any higher than that authorized by this committee for fiscal year 1965." Joint Committee on Atomic Energy, *Authorizing Appropriations for the Atomic Energy Commission for Fiscal Year 1965,* S. Rept. 987, 88 Cong. 2 sess. (1964), p. 27.

Aided by the expunction of the MURA accelerator, the resultant study submitted by the AEC in January 1965 trimmed anticipated future expenditures from the annual level of $572-$607 million that the Ramsey panel had recommended for 1975-81 down to a mere $450-$490 million. However, President Johnson refrained from endorsing this long term plan, declaring, "The needs for the long-range future, as visualized today, will undoubtedly change with time. We must not be so bound to our guidelines that there is no flexibility to respond to the changing needs of the program, and to changing fiscal needs and resources." See *High Energy Physics Program: Report on National Policy and Background Information,* Joint Committee on Atomic Energy, 89 Cong. 1 sess. (February 1965), pp. 1, 48, and 108.

are in a budgetary enclave of their own and are not judged competitively with the proposals of university faculty. This is a correct statement of the situation, since laboratory basic research is programmed mainly by the scientist himself, with the approval of his superiors and the laboratory director; he does not, like the university professor, have to submit an independent proposal to the AEC, for his funds come out of the multi-million dollar laboratory budget negotiated annually by contractor representatives and the AEC. Laboratory officials concede that their basic research projects are less subject to competitive review than are those of university departments, but contend this is as it should be: "I would justify this strongly as necessary for us to do a good job on the applied work for which we are hired," said one laboratory director. "An AEC panel reviewing [basic] research should not evaluate a scientist here on general scientific criteria which apply to university scientists generally, but rather on the degree to which his basic research helps advance the overall program of this laboratory." An erstwhile university administrator suggested, more crudely, that much of the basic research of applied laboratories was simply "a fringe benefit for staff."

There is merit to this argument, but it can be carried too far. No doubt, the value of some basic research at Los Alamos, Argonne, or Oak Ridge should be judged by how well it advances the laboratory's practical missions; but if the work is mediocre, it will not advance that mission as much as better work, nor attract better scientists to the laboratory. And if a particular field of knowledge is a necessary or desirable foundation for a development program, would it not be preferable to establish contact with the best men in that field, wherever they may be, through consultantships and subcontracts for research? The laboratories evidently use consultants with some frequency, but make relatively little use of subcontracting,[12] which might profitably be extended. Ultimately, there is no escaping the test of quality, and it is difficult to see why basic research at AEC laboratories should not pass that test as rigorously as that at universities.

[12] In FY 1965, for example, Argonne subcontracted $2,600,000 of R&D; the Lawrence Radiation Laboratory, $1,840,000; Los Alamos, $134,000; and Brookhaven, $23,000; virtually none of this was for basic research.

AEC and laboratory spokesmen are not disposed to accept this line of argument. "On the average," one declared, "the basic work of the laboratories is at least as good as the average in the universities. Moreover, the scrutiny given internally by management and its advisers is a real thing." In addition, the quality of laboratory research is tested by eminent visiting committees, who report to the laboratory director and/or contractor. While their evaluation is after-the-fact, before-the-fact review by special committees often occurs when a laboratory proposes a new program or a significant program expansion. Consultants, laboratory directors believe, cannot substitute for experts on the spot. ". . . we must carefully consider the problem of getting qualified research people outside the laboratory committed to and involved in the early stages of development which often follows relevant research," one director observed. "Our experience shows subcontracting to be generally ineffective in this regard."

Nuclear Weapons Development

Although the national and international significance of their work has given the weapons laboratories great political, technical, and budgetary strength—in FY 1964, the operating budgets of Sandia, Livermore, and Los Alamos were the largest of all AEC laboratories (Table 9)—they have, nonetheless, experienced several marked cycles of achievement, enthusiasm, and confidence. Los Alamos' great wartime[13] era was succeeded by a phase of calamities during which the great names departed, water gave out, morale ebbed, things were "in a state of disintegration,"[14] and serious consideration was given to abandoning the site and relocating closer to civi-

[13] The wartime laboratory has been variously extolled as "Athens," "a miracle of a laboratory," "as nearly perfect as I have ever seen . . . a big laboratory," and "the best laboratory in the world" by, respectively, an unnamed experimental physicist, Rabi, Bethe, and Oppenheimer. See Daniel Lang, *An Inquiry into Enoughness* (McGraw-Hill, New York, 1965), p. 355; *In the Matter of J. Robert Oppenheimer,* Hearing, Personnel Security Board, Atomic Energy Commission (1954), p. 457; *Science* (April 12, 1963), p. 162; and *Investigation into the United States Atomic Energy Project,* Hearings before Joint Committee on Atomic Energy, 81 Cong. 1 sess. (1949), p. 301.

[14] According to Hans Bethe. See *In the Matter of J. Robert Oppenheimer, op. cit.,* p. 333.

lization. Morale revived as the laboratory's permanence became assured and the construction required to lend stability and promise both to life in the community and to research in the laboratory was undertaken. Soon, the spur of imperious goals was again imparted by events—Russia's explosion of a nuclear bomb in 1949, the pursuit of a hydrogen bomb announced by President Truman in January 1950, the outbreak of the Korean War in June 1950 that gave that pursuit a sense of urgency, the expansion of production which confirmed that urgency, and Russia's 1953 explosion of an airborne hydrogen bomb which heightened it. As the pace quickened, recruitment expanded, some of the wartime giants— Teller, Wheeler, Bethe, even von Neumann and Fermi, on occasions—returned to the fold for stretches of time; and, starting March 1950, the laboratory went on a six day week for almost three years.

Unfortunately, this new drive, which culminated in 1956 in the successful testing of a hydrogen bomb dropped from an airplane,[15] was not marked by the unity of scientific effort that had characterized the wartime enterprise. The cleavages within the Commission and the scientific community about the desirability of proceeding with the hydrogen bomb were succeeded by cleavages as to who should be responsible for developing it, the most likely avenues to success, and whether a new weapons laboratory should be established, as it finally was at Livermore in July 1952 under the leadership of Edward Teller, Ernest Lawrence, and Herbert York. These bitter conflicts, which led even to public aspersions on the loyalty of Los Alamos scientists and the genuineness of their interest in bomb development, shook morale at the mother laboratory so that special efforts, including a July 1954 citation from President Eisenhower,[16] were made to restore it.

[15] "It was in the summer of 1953 that . . . [Russia] announced . . . that she had successfully tested the first airborne thermonuclear . . .weapon, . . . dropped from a giant bomber, whereas our tests in November 1952 and in March 1954 were of clumsy earthbound devices. . . . Indeed, it was not until May 1956 . . . that we finally succeeded in exploding a hydrogen bomb dropped from a B-52. . . . between August 1953 and May 1956 the Soviet Union was the only power . . . possessing a stockpile of hydrogen bombs." William Laurence, *Men and Atoms* (Simon and Schuster, New York, 1959), pp. 180-81.

[16] The citation stated, in part, that "The Laboratory's momentous success in the

By its own admission, the new laboratory at Livermore "started badly. In the first couple of years they had some failures in weapons tests at Nevada and in the Pacific. Things had gotten too radical. They went back to their homework. They became experts. (An expert, says Teller, paraphrasing Niels Bohr, is a man who had made all the mistakes.) Soon their designs began to work."[17] Though most of the nuclear weapons in the present national stockpile originated at Los Alamos, "the input from Livermore today [1962] equals that from Los Alamos";[18] Livermore's contribution has been paramount particularly in the development of warheads for strategic missiles such as the Air Force's Minuteman and the Navy's Polaris.

Morale at the laboratories has naturally been affected by their confidence in the future, governed in the first instance by their zest for their work and, in the last, by its national significance (or the degree to which that significance, real and illusory, has been recognized and supported by the nation's leaders).

Does a laboratory have an "attitude," outlook, or atmosphere, determined by circumstances, history, and the disposition of its director and senior staff? Informed observers talk as if this were so, and a visitor can neither escape his own impressions nor avoid contrasting Los Alamos and Livermore. Thus, the former is characterized kindly as more mature and balanced or unkindly as older and more tired; the latter, either as "hotter" and more exciting or wilder and more extreme.[19] At Sandia, entered through what looks

---

field of fission weapons has been followed by equal accomplishments in the fusion field. These achievements are the result of a remarkable group endeavor and the devoted and skillful effort of the individuals of the staff of the Laboratory." See *Seventeenth Semiannual Report,* Atomic Energy Commission (January 1955), p. 15.

[17] From Daniel Wilkes, "Far Out with the Atom," Lawrence Radiation Laboratory, Livermore (1962). Cf. Edward Teller: "We were told to go ahead on the [thermonuclear bomb] program and were given a charter to do something new which required major advancements in science and technology. We tried and we failed. Then we tried again and we failed again. At that time any reasonable management would have shut us down, but the AEC management was not reasonable, the management was good. They recognized that something new cannot be accomplished without taking risks and we were encouraged to experiment further. The next time we succeeded" (in *Aviation Week and Space Technology,* April 22, 1963, p. 101).

[18] Wilkes, *vid. supra.*

[19] Cf. Brig. Gen. Crowson, Director of the Division of Military Applications: "You have to recognize the fact that LASL [Los Alamos] is generally more conservative as

like stainless steel sliding bars, the impression is of an iron rigor and reliability, as befits an organization responsible for seeing that nuclear weapons explode only when they are supposed to and under no other conceivable condition.

Already in 1952, AEC Chairman Gordon Dean observed that

> . . . the current atomic arms race cannot go on forever. Somewhere along the line there is a point where the law of diminishing returns begins to operate. And somewhere, not too far beyond this point, there is another point where we will have acquired all of the weapons we would possibly need. . . .
>
> When this point is reached, and it is not in the unforeseeable future, the question arises: "What do we do then?" Do we go on turning out more and more fissionable material and more and more weapons, as we are doing now? Or do we say to ourselves, "Now we have enough; no matter how many bombs our competitor may choose to make, we have enough."
>
> I think we should do the latter.[20]

And in 1955 Alvin Weinberg, director of the Oak Ridge Laboratory, foresaw "an approach to saturation in our military technology. . . . Should technological saturation be achieved, as it just about has [sic] in . . . big explosives, then our big military technological research institutions will hardly retain their original validity."[21]

Until 1952, Los Alamos worked exclusively on weapons, but by 1955, some 10 percent of its $35 million budget was devoted to basic research, reactors, and other activities. "Some of the people here are getting weary of weapons work," a 1955 visitor was told. ". . . the weapons program would benefit in the long run if the scientists here could take a break now and then to work on something else."[22] "Can you improve a toothbrush indefinitely?" Los

---

far as management is concerned. You have to recognize that LRL [Livermore] at times takes the shotgun approach to a problem and puts 40 or 50 people on it whereas LASL will use 1." *AEC Authorizing Legislation Fiscal Year 1966*, Hearings before the Joint Committee on Atomic Energy, 89 Cong. 1 sess. (1965), Pt. 1, p. 139.

[20] In *Atomic Power and Private Enterprise*, Joint Committee on Atomic Energy, 82 Cong. 2 sess. (1952), p. 11.

[21] Alvin Weinberg, "Future Aims of Large Scale Research," *Chemical and Engineering News* (May 23, 1955), p. 2189.

[22] From the record of a 1955 interview with a well qualified Los Alamos informant made available to the writer.

Alamos physicist John Manley asked.[23] By 1964, 45 percent of the laboratory's $85.5 million budget went into nonweapons programs, the largest of which was concerned with the development of a reactor for space propulsion (nonetheless, there had been an absolute increase in weapons expenditures, over the decade, to $47.5 million). At Livermore, in 1964, the weapons program consumed $83.5 million or 78 percent of the laboratory budget, the remainder going for work on controlled hydrogen fusion, a nuclear ramjet missile, the use of nuclear explosives for excavation and mining, and biological research. At Sandia, there has been less diversification, although much more than is commonly known or acknowledged. (In fiscal year 1967, according to one informant, 14 percent of Sandia's work was conducted for other agencies, mainly the Defense Department and NASA.) Some opportunities have been rejected to conduct for other agencies work which the laboratory was singularly well justified to do; others have been accepted and still others are being explored.

The advent of the missile era enlarged the range of fruitful R&D on nuclear weapons. AEC laboratories played a critical role in launching that era by reducing the weight of warheads,[24] and their work in ensuring the reliability of these warheads under the exotic conditions and severe stresses to which they are subjected has been indispensable to the introduction, improvement, and maintenance of new delivery systems. And the laboratories do not only spend money; they may even, in the larger calculus of military expenditures, save some, for a reduction in the weight of a warhead can lead to economies in the vehicles which transport it.

[23] See Daniel Lang, *From Hiroshima to the Moon* (Simon and Schuster, New York, 1959), p. 356.

[24] "Deeply concerned in 1953 at the previous lack of attention given to missile development, my administration quickly turned to outstanding scientists and engineers to determine the feasibility of developing effective weapons of this character. On February 10, 1954, one of those scientific groups, headed by Dr. John von Neumann, reported the possibility of a major breakthrough—as the result of AEC research—in reducing the size of missile warheads and recommended development of a correspondingly designed intercontinental ballistic missile (ICBM). . . . it takes about two hundred pounds of launching weight to put one pound of warhead on target several thousand miles away, and . . . the first atomic warheads weighed nine thousand pounds. . . ." Dwight D. Eisenhower, *Waging Peace, 1956-1961; the White House Years* (Doubleday & Co., Garden City, N.Y., 1965), p. 208.

How far into the future this process of weapons improvement may usefully go, and what budgetary level is necessary to sustain it, are questions that cannot be answered without examination of classified information. Clearly, however, there are, among those conversant with that information, significant differences of opinion about what the answers should be.

In 1960, the Commission declared its intent to ensure that the three weapons laboratories will be ". . . maintained as strong and vigorous institutions. Should there be some decrease in weapon research and development needs, consideration will be given to expanding these laboratories' nonweapon functions. . . . As far as practical such expansion will be in the fields requiring talents comparable with those needed for weapons development."[25] Speaking for the Nuclear Energy Committee of the National Association of Manufacturers, Lauchlin Currie responded that "the Commission's intent to maintain personnel strength of weapons laboratories even if international agreements are reached . . . we are strongly opposed to, since it smacks of a 'make work' philosophy which is . . . wasteful and uneconomic. . . ."[26] And the AEC's own General Advisory Committee observed that ". . . should the scientists in these laboratories be assigned to nonweapons research for a period of 10 to 20 years, we would no longer have capable standby weapons scientists. After such a period, one probably could organize more effective weapons research and development by bringing together able and vigorous younger scientists as was done in World War II."[27]

President Kennedy himself appeared to adopt a similar position about the need for weapons research and weapons testing to maintain the viability of the laboratories. In the March 1962 national address in which he explained his authorization for the resumption of atmospheric tests following the Soviet Union's breach of the test moratorium the previous September, he declared:

. . . in actual practice, particularly in a society of free choice, we cannot keep top-flight scientists concentrating on the preparation of an experiment which may or may not take place on an uncertain date in

[25] See *The Future Role of the Atomic Energy Commission Laboratories, op. cit.*, p. 33.
[26] *Ibid.*, p. 242.
[27] *Ibid.*, p. 245.

the undefined future. Nor can large technical laboratories be kept fully alert on a stand-by basis waiting for some other nation to break an agreement. This is not merely difficult or inconvenient—we have explored this alternative thoroughly, and found it impossible of execution.[28]

Subsequently, as part of his effort to win Senate approval for the 1963 treaty banning atmospheric nuclear tests, Kennedy, accepting the four safeguards recommended by the Joint Chiefs of Staff, pledged that the government would continue underground testing "vigorously and diligently," "maintain . . . readiness" to resume atmospheric tests, expand facilities for the detection of treaty violations, and "maintain strong weapons laboratories in a vigorous program of weapons development. . . ."[29] These pledges have been honored and led to large increases in expenditures on weapons development, due to the expense of the extensive underground tests which the laboratories have been conducting, mainly at the Nevada test site some 70 miles northwest of Las Vegas.

Nevertheless, it cannot be said that the laboratories are quite happy with their lot. For their drive to improve our nuclear offen-

[28] *Public Papers of the Presidents . . . John F. Kennedy, 1962*, p. 191.

[29] The passages of Kennedy's Sept. 10, 1963 letter to Senators Mansfield and Dirksen dealing with the weapons laboratories went as follows:

"1. Underground nuclear testing, which is permitted under the treaty, will be vigorously and diligently carried forward, and the equipment, facilities, personnel and funds necessary for that purpose will be provided. As the Senate knows, such testing is now going on. While we must all hope that at some future time a more comprehensive treaty may become possible by changes in the policies of other nations, until that time our underground testing program will continue.

"2. The United States will maintain a posture of readiness to resume testing in the environments prohibited by the present treaty. . . .

"3. Our facilities for the detection of possible violations of this treaty will be expanded and improved as required to increase our insurance against clandestine violation by others. . . .

"7. This Government will maintain strong weapons laboratories in a vigorous program of weapons development, in order to ensure that the United States will continue to have in the future a strength fully adequate for an effective national defense. . . .

"8. The United States will diligently pursue its programs for the further development of nuclear explosives for peaceful purposes by underground tests within the terms of the treaty, and as and when such developments make possible constructive uses of atmospheric nuclear explosions for peaceful purposes, the United States will seek international agreement under the treaty to permit such explosions. . . ." *Public Papers of the Presidents of the United States, John F. Kennedy, 1963* (Washington, D.C., 1964), pp. 670-71.

sive and defensive technology runs inherently counter to efforts at
the highest levels of national policy to stabilize or even dismantle
that technology by international agreement. Thus, a prolonged
ban on all nuclear tests would pose a real crisis. Even with the
present program of underground tests, the laboratories have experienced difficulty recruiting first-rate staff. "The chief reason, it
seems, is that few young scientists and engineers regard nuclear
weapons work as the cutting edge of science as it was when Fermi
and Oppenheimer . . . were at Los Alamos."[30] "The battle for nuclear weapons is a lot tougher now . . . a lot of people . . . find the
whole matter distasteful," a Livermore spokesman acknowledged.
"Nobody likes to work in a bomb factory," said the laboratory director, John Foster.[31] The chief inducement is a conviction that
the work is important. "Foster says, in effect, that his people must
believe that their contributions have an influence on the changing
balance of power."[32] How long can that belief be sustained?

New Nuclear Technology

In principle, AEC laboratories are not to go beyond the line that
divides the development of new technology from its systematic
production; or they are to do so only temporarily, until private
industry demonstrates its capacity—or, rather (because of the statutory proscription of monopoly), until at least *two* private, competitive companies demonstrate their capacity to provide the new nuclear product or service.[33]

But just where is that line to be drawn? After some tens of
thousands of weapons, we may reasonably speak of a production
"process," although, as one informant remarked, ". . . it is still a
Swiss-watch operation"; and the same is surely true of the dozens
of pressurized water reactors that have been—should one say "produced" or "fabricated"—for the Navy's nuclear submarines. These

[30] Howard Simons and Chalmers Roberts, "Our Bomb Factories Looking for Love,"
Washington Post (April 25, 1965), Sec. E, p. 3.

[31] *Ibid.*, p. 1.

[32] *Ibid.*, p. 3.

[33] Ernest Tremmel, Director of the AEC Division of Industrial Participation, has,
however, observed that (twins aside) you can't have two children without first having
one.

are precision assemblies of unusual components machined in small batches to fantastic tolerance and reliability requirements, with the design of components and the whole assembly being frequently modified to incorporate improvements effected in the laboratory, the production facility, or at some other point along the line from the uranium mine to the submarine hold. Such highly skilled, frequently modified operations are characteristic of the nuclear industry.

Most of the key scientists, managers, engineers, and technicians in the industry have worked, at one time or another, in government facilities. Although the private industry remains dependent upon the stream of technical information and services supplied by the laboratories and cannot rival their $1.2 billion investment in plant and equipment,[34] it has gradually acquired a respectable R&D competence of its own, and expansion of this competence is one way by which significant product improvement can occur. Government R&D—and, of late, operating—contracts have also been sought and, to some extent, openly utilized to nurse along a competitive industry until it could be sustained by a higher and more regular volume of production orders from government and private sources, at home and abroad. In its Power Reactor Demonstration Program, the AEC has explicitly utilized R&D contracts and design assistance as a form of financial encouragement ("subsidy" is the harsher but no less accurate word) to the private nuclear industry. These and other factors argue for drawing the line in laboratory programs further back from the developmental end of the scale and correspondingly increasing the volume of applied research and development contracting with private industry; and, of course, this is what private industry with an R&D capability would like to see. A 1961 survey by the Atomic Industrial Forum of the attitudes of member firms toward the role of government laboratories in the civilian nuclear power program found that vir-

[34] Including $934.5 million completed plant and equipment and $282.6 million estimated cost of projects under construction or authorized as of June 30, 1963 at the Lawrence Radiation, Los Alamos, Argonne, Brookhaven, and Oak Ridge laboratories as well as facilities of these laboratories located at the Nevada Test Site and the National Reactor Test Station. See *1963 Financial Report,* Atomic Energy Commission, pp. 47-52. To be sure, much of this investment is for pure research or bomb development facilities that would be of no commercial interest to industry.

TABLE 10

AEC Research and Development Expenditures by Sector, 1958–65

(In percentages)

Sector	Reactors								All fields but weapons[a]		
	1958	1959	1960	1961	1962	1963	1964	1965	1963	1964	1965
Private industry	17	23	26	27	31	35	39	38	23	25	22
AEC laboratories[b]	82	75	72	71	65	61	57	56	64	62	64
Universities	c	c	c	1	1	1	1	1	10	9	9
Other nonprofit	1	c	1	1	1	1	1	1	2	1	1
Other government	c	1	1	1	2	2	3	5	2	3	4
Total	100	100	100	100	100	100	100	100	100	100	100
Millions of dollars	$290	$326	$362	$425	$397	$462	$502	$478	$738	$798	$826

Source: AEC *Annual Report* for 1965, p. 40; 1963, p. 303; and 1961, p. 32. A refinement of this table for 1961-63, kindly provided by the AEC, reports the distribution of those reactor development expenditures that might contribute most to fostering a private nuclear industry (i.e., expenditures on general reactor technology, advanced systems, and nuclear safety were excluded). Of these more narrowly defined expenditures totaling $845 million in 1961, $321 million in 1962, and $358 million in 1963, private industry received 25, 32, and 38 percent, respectively; and AEC laboratories, 73, 65, and 60 percent.

[a] Included, in 1964, the following expenditures in millions of dollars: reactor development 502; physical research, 204; biology and medicine, 71; isotope development, 8; peaceful explosives, 13.

[b] Government-owned, contractor-operated.

[c] Less than .5%.

tually all firms endorsed the laboratories' conduct of "long-range basic research," but a majority of reactor manufacturers favored a shift in government R&D funds from the laboratories to private facilities. Such a shift was, however, opposed by a majority of architect-engineering firms and private utilities.[35]

The AEC, itself, has declared that "increased responsibility will continue to be placed on industrial organizations to perform Commission-supported development, as the nuclear energy field progresses toward commercial application and as private organizations acquire capability in facilities and personnel";[36] and the proportion of reactor research and development expenditures at private industrial facilities has risen over the years, while that at AEC laboratories (including not only the multi-program but other government laboratories) has declined. However, in recent years, the laboratories still received roughly three-fifths of all funds, not only for reactor R&D, but for all nonweapons R&D (Table 10) and, as reactor expenditures have stabilized in the mid-1960's, this situation is unlikely to change markedly. Budgetary constraints render more acute the need to clarify the respective functions of public and private laboratories in the development of civilian nuclear technology.

One industry representative criticized the AEC laboratories for taking an academic rather than a practical approach to their work. Why have so many—"someone once calculated 240"—different reactor concepts been pursued? The laboratories should concentrate instead, he suggested, on fewer concepts and on lines of research more help to and less competitive with private industry, such as improving radiation standards or ensuring reactor safety at reduced cost. Their guiding principle should be not the development of new technology at all points on the compass, but the identification and solution of specific technical and economic problems faced by industry. From the standpoint of a private firm with an established nuclear business, the worst of all AEC activities are too

---

[35] See *A Summary of Forum Member Views on Atomic Energy Development Compiled by the Forum Staff*, Supplement I to the Report of the Ad Hoc Committee on Atomic Policy of the Atomic Industrial Forum (Atomic Industrial Forum, New York, 1962), p. 17; see also pp. 46-47 and 54.

[36] *The Future Role of the Atomic Energy Commission Laboratories, op. cit.*, p. 32.

rapid and too successful developments rendering obsolete existing investments.[37]

While there is a great deal of sense in the foregoing position, its complete acceptance as general AEC policy would turn the laboratories essentially into handmaidens of industry in the realm of civilian technology, whereas, surely, the objective of public laboratories should be to serve exclusively the interests neither of industry nor of science, but of the broader public. This requires that, at least until the technology of nuclear reactors becomes as safe and standardized as that of typewriters, government laboratories maintain the competence not merely to supplement and help private industry, but to pace and monitor its performance in the interests of the national health and safety.

While such a role involves a certain amount of competition and overlap with industry, that amount could be reduced as the number of qualified nuclear firms increases. The present need appears to be to enlarge the scale and scope of industrial R&D while sharpening the direction of the laboratories' technological activities.

Where laboratories compete with industry in applied research and development, and with universities in basic and applied research, the optimal balance between the volume of work conducted in government and in private facilities will inevitably be struck both by objective and political considerations. At the present juncture, in our opinion, the balance with regard to major basic research facilities should be tilted toward laboratories operated by fraternities of universities to ensure their availability to all qualified scientists; while the balance in the conduct of applied research and development should be tilted toward private industrial laboratories, to encourage the growth of private nuclear industry. (This is not to suggest that industry should not also be encouraged, through direct contracts and indirect incentives, to

[37] "It seems strange to see a complaint . . . that the exploration of new technical concepts is detrimental to progress," observes one national laboratory reader. "A most important factor is being overlooked, namely, that a maximum exchange of ideas between the National Laboratories and industry must take place, followed by joint participation in advanced development. . . . The AEC is making great efforts to promote this type of cooperation, but it will succeed only if industry plays its part. . . ."

conduct that kind of "basic" or "background" research which has proved so helpful to the development of radically new "science based" technologies.)

One way of deciding on relatively objective grounds how the balance should be struck in any particular scientific or technical area is to encourage more frequent competition between governmental and private sectors. The proposal of Dan Kimball, president of the Aerojet-General Corporation, that industry be given the opportunity "to freely compete for research and development programs as well as hardware developments which under current practices would be assigned to the Commission laboratories by administrative directive"[38] seems reasonable. The emphasis should be on *program* competition—i.e., on giving the industrial (and, in appropriate circumstances, the academic) sector an opportunity to make a case for handling a new program, before the final "sectoral" decision is made by the AEC. For such intersectoral competition to work, both private and government laboratories must be kept abreast of emergent AEC program interests. As the Atomic Industrial Forum has observed, "In the case of the AEC laboratories, the annual budget submission serves as a periodic device for the laboratories to learn of the AEC's intentions for the future and to make known their own ideas and proposals for funding projects. No such regular mechanism exists for industry (or universities), either to contribute its own ideas and proposals or to become informed on the AEC's future R&D program plans and objectives."[39] To promote such industrial participation, one informant suggested that the laboratories be required to prepare and

[38] *The Future Role . . . , op. cit.,* p. 161.

[39] See *The Future Role . . . , op. cit.,* p. 235. The Office (now, Division) of Industrial Participation was established in 1961 after discussions with a task force of the U. S. Chamber of Commerce, partly to serve this function of alerting industry to AEC and laboratory plans before commitments were made about whether, and where the work should be conducted. However, its separation from AEC program divisions has limited its effectiveness so that Commissioner James Ramey could subsequently state that "the AEC is in need of more regularized means of hearing about industry's problems and needs. . . . Our Divisions of Reactor Development and Industrial Participation are making valiant efforts in this direction, but more remains to be done." *Development, Growth, and State of the Atomic Energy Industry,* Hearings before the Joint Committee on Atomic Energy, 88 Cong. 1 sess. (Feb. 20 and 21, 1963), Pt. 1, p. 289.

make publicly available five year plans for their unclassified work. It is true, industry and universities have budget cycles similar to the laboratories, in which they advance their plans and can learn something about the AEC's intentions; but as the scope of their work is usually narrower, so is their knowledge.

To be sure, knowledge alone is insufficient, and industry leaders who *are* well informed regard it as insignificant. In their view, *money* is significant, and industry has been hurt in recent years not by its lack of information but by tight budgets which, restraining a general expansion, have led the AEC to assign to its laboratories certain work that might otherwise have gone to industry. (The laboratories, for their part, assert that most of their work is not *assigned* but merely *approved* by the Commission—i.e., that the ideas originate internally. "If industry wants to compete in the marginal area," said one laboratory spokesman, "then *they* have to come up with the ideas.")

Dissemination of New Knowledge

The laboratories' function of developing improved and economic nuclear technology can be exercised successfully only by the timely dissemination of new scientific and technical knowledge to the universities and industry. In addition to the normal means of disseminating such knowledge by professional and trade publications and participation in scientific and industrial meetings, special programs have been instituted at the laboratories (or at Germantown, with the laboratories' assistance) to make this knowledge more widely available. These include the preparation, publication, and extensive distribution of books, monographs, and periodic reviews of the status of various scientific and technical fields; the organization of conferences; the establishment of specialized information and data centers; and the production of technical and semi-technical films. Other measures which, directly or indirectly, serve the same purpose are: special training institutes; the encouragement of university faculty and graduate students to conduct research at the laboratories; and the acceptance of employees from private firms to work temporarily beside laboratory staff on projects of interest to their firm. Recently, offices of industrial cooperation have been established, first at Oak Ridge and, subsequently (in January 1965), at Argonne, to provide a point of contact and assistance for private industry and to stimulate use of AEC-developed technology by such means as advertisements in trade journals, conferences, and consulting services. Within the limits of conflict-of-interest regulations, laboratory staff have also served as consultants to private industry.

In the past, the development of civilian nuclear technology was undoubtedly hampered by stringent security controls. Writing in 1953, directly after his term as AEC chairman, Gordon Dean stated that "Industry must . . . have some assurance that there will be a relaxation of the present Commission regulations relating to secrecy, so that it can gain access to the information it needs to design, build, and operate reactors. . . . there should be a broad declassification of reactor information in the interest of speedy progress toward the goal of economically feasible power."[40] In 1955, classification policies were revised, opening up large areas of reactor information and reducing from more secret categories to "confidential" much that remained classified;[41] in the same year, an "access permit" system was introduced under which companies could obtain information classified up to "confidential," and, in certain circumstances, some categories of "secret" material. But complaints against security restrictions continued. Thus, in 1955, Senator Clinton Anderson criticized the "unnecessary restraints" of the access permit system, charging that "it is easier for a camel to pass through the eye of a needle than it is for a businessman to receive frank and complete and unfettered answers from the Atomic Energy Commission."[42] And, in 1956, Arnold Kramish and former Commissioner Eugene Zuckert declared:

It is difficult to see how the nuclear power business can ever be put on a sound economic footing as long as technological data directly related to costs is kept behind this thin security veil of a "Confidential" classification available to almost all comers but not subject to public

[40] Gordon Dean, *Report on the Atom* (Knopf, New York, 1953), p. 171.

[41] See Lewis L. Strauss, *Men and Decisions* (Doubleday, Garden City, N. Y., 1962), p. 327.

[42] Cited in Harold Green and Alan Rosenthal, *Government of the Atom* (Atherton Press, New York, 1963), p. 205, footnote.

discussion or reporting in the technical, trade, financial, or daily press . . . the hazards in the Access Permit system are too great to risk acceptance of such a system as a continuing practice.[43]

As the years have gone by, restrictions have eased, technical and price data have become more freely available, and complaints at security controls have correspondingly diminished. Such complaints as remain have shifted from the sphere of civilian reactor technology to that of nuclear space propulsion, systems for nuclear auxiliary power, the peaceful use of atomic explosives, and the uranium enrichment process. However, it was the general judgment of AEC staff and officials at laboratories conducting classified work that, if the entire security system could be eliminated, the volume of civilian nuclear industrial applications would rise only slightly—"by 10 percent, not ten times," one informant estimated. Some confirmation of this view may be found in the evident loss of industrial interest in the access permit program, use of which has declined so substantially, as the volume of technical information in the open literature has increased, that consideration has been given to discontinuing it.

One essential information function of the AEC laboratories has been to foster a competitive private nuclear industry and to restrain the development of monopoly in any major sector of the industry. The program of disseminating technical information and, more important, the maintenance of large laboratory staffs capable of generating this information and of training and advising private firms is, accordingly, a device not merely for creating a new industry but for shaping its economic structure.

How successful that device has been is another matter. Had a highly concentrated reactor industry arisen solely as the result of

[43] Arnold Kramish and Eugene Zuckert, *Atomic Energy for Your Business* (David McKay, New York, 1956), p. 175. Cf. John Palfrey's similar criticism at the time: "A number of informed observers . . . now regard the elimination of secrecy in this field as indispensable. They have concluded that the development of commercial power will be greatly retarded until the whole field of reactor technology is declassified, and the hindrances of personnel and physical security eliminated. From the competitive viewpoint, the argument is particularly persuasive. It is certainly clear that the favored position of the insiders is accentuated as long as information available to them is not freely available to others." "Atomic Energy: A New Experiment in Government-Industry Relations," *Columbia Law Review* (1956), Vol. 56, No. 3, pp. 383-84.

private enterprise, the government might have confined itself to action in the courts to prevent monopoly and to various forms of regulation to protect public health and safety. The maintenance of numerous large laboratories simply to afford private investors an opportunity to enter the nuclear industry and thereby preserve its tenuous competitive status might well be deemed an expensive demonstration of economic principle.

Technical Advice

The multi-program laboratories are a ready resource to Commission staff seeking an informed judgment about the merit of an unsolicited basic research proposal from a university scientist or a proposal solicited from an industrial laboratory for a purpose specified by the AEC. Although, upon occasion, laboratory staff may act as technical consultants to an AEC contract selection board, they cannot, as private employees, serve on the board itself.

It is normal practice for AEC staff administering basic research programs in the physical and biological sciences to consult, and send contract proposals for review by, eminent scientists at universities and at those contractor-operated laboratories with which the Commission has had long-standing associations. The staff's function is to marry the best scientific advice they can obtain to the practical realities of AEC budgets and program interests.

In the area of civilian nuclear—and particularly reactor—technology, attempts have been made in recent years to strengthen the role of the multi-program laboratories in program planning and administration. Alvin Weinberg, director of the Oak Ridge laboratory, has suggested that "the national laboratories . . . could and should be drawn into the management, as well as into the conduct, of Government-applied research and development to a much greater extent than they now are."[44] Aside from making more use of laboratory scientists in an informal advisory capacity, there are two principal ways by which this could be done: the assignment of laboratory staff for tours of duty at regional or national AEC

[44] See statement of Alvin Weinberg, Nov. 20, 1963, in *Federal Research and Development Programs*, Hearings before the House Select Committee on Government Research, Under the Authority of H. Res. 504, 88 Cong. 2 sess. (1964), Pt. 1, p. 320.

offices; and the assignment to AEC laboratories of advisory responsibilities for all or part of designated AEC programs. The former approach has been elaborated by Weinberg:

> On the whole, since the highest salaries are paid by the contractors, the most mature, experienced people are in the contractor establishments, not in the Government. Can we not devise some scheme whereby the tremendous pool of talent in the contractor establishments can be brought more directly to bear on technical decisions of Government? What I have in mind is to encourage people in places such as Oak Ridge National Laboratory . . . to work for periods of 2 or 3 years for . . . the Atomic Energy Commission directly. We now do this, but because of various conflict-of-interest regulations, and differences in salary scales, such tours of duty are difficult to arrange.
>
> What is needed is a much freer back-and-forth flow between the Government and at least some of its contractor establishments than is now possible, a restoration, if you will, of the spirit and style of research during World War II. At that time managers of the Radiation Laboratory . . . each of whom was an MIT employee, entered intimately and directly into the most important policy deliberations of the Armed Forces. Arthur Compton (head of the Chicago Metallurgical Laboratory) and E. O. Lawrence (head of the Berkeley Radiation Laboratory) served in the closest possible liaison with General Groves in mapping the technical course of the Manhattan project. I realize that today there are many difficulties in achieving this relation; yet I believe it is ever so worthwhile. . . .[45]

Such a freer exchange between government and private employment has much to commend it, since it would bring to the AEC men of scientific distinction and/or practical experience, and to the laboratories, men familiar with the broad range of AEC interests. The practical problems of maintaining salaries, seniority, and employment benefits during the exchange period can probably be solved—following the series of substantial government wage increases in recent years, the old refrain about low salaries preventing the government from employing the best men has lost some force, except for the highest priced administrative and scientific talent. One commentator observed, "I know of many instances in which senior contractor personnel have actually made the transition to government service with an increase in salary. Therefore

[45] *Ibid.*, p. 319.

the freer exchange between public and private employment . . . is actually more feasible and is taking place to . . . [a considerable] extent, . . ." Potential conflict of interest presents a more recalcitrant problem. Doubtless, it can be dealt with by the choice of the right men through equitable and open application procedures, and their use in assignments from which their company can derive no commercial advantage. However, the charges or suspicion of "conflict of interest" may remain a persistent source of discomfort.

The second approach, of assigning to a multi-program laboratory responsibility for managing a civilian technology program, has been pursued increasingly. While the Commission has long prided itself on maintaining a relatively small staff,[46] it has, at times, had to acknowledge the inadequacy of this staff to direct certain development programs: ". . . we have not in every instance . . . had the adequate technical strength that we need to evaluate proposed [reactor] projects, to review the technical progress, and to maintain the independent surveillance of contractor performance that we would like to have. . . . We have not been able to increase the numbers to the extent we would like to have in a number of areas," Assistant General Manager Dwight Ink told the Joint Committee in May 1962.[47]

A member of the Division of Reactor Development asserted more bluntly, shortly thereafter, that "we say we make the final decisions but we're really a captive of industry because we don't have the technical people to second-guess industry." In an effort to cope with this problem, the Commission has "adopted the general

[46] Cf. "The Federal Diary" by Jerry Kluttz:

"President Johnson has rejected an offer of . . . the Atomic Energy Commission, to cut its staff by 1 percent in spite of his appeals to all agencies to economize by reducing both dollars and jobs. . . .

"AEC has a budget of $2.7 billion for this year but only $73 million of it is used to maintain a staff of 7000 direct employees to administer the huge program. The President noted that the agency's staff had increased only 3 percent during the past eight years despite a 400 percent increase in work associated with peaceful uses of the atom. . . .

"In rejecting the agency's offer . . . . the President directed that the employees be used 'to ride herd' on the 128,000 contract workers and their employers to see that they do a good job for Uncle Sam." *Washington Post* (April 30, 1964).

[47] See *AEC Authorizing Legislation Fiscal Year 1963*, Hearings before the Subcommittee on Legislation of the Joint Committee on Atomic Energy, 87 Cong. 2 sess. (May 29, 1962), p. 413.

policy of having some national laboratory assigned to each different type of reactor, to be on top of it, to know the technical facts, and assist us in directing it."[48]

The private nuclear industry has not exactly welcomed this increased managerial role for the AEC laboratories. One industry executive characterized the laboratories as "empire builders," and stated frankly that, although "We've been directed several times to go down to a laboratory and tell them everything . . . there is a tendency to hold back" some key technical information, for fear that the laboratory will either exploit it or pass it on to an industrial competitor. Another informant, criticizing the quality of engineering work, observed that one laboratory "hasn't been able to make a reactor which works." Others have objected to the assumption of managerial responsibilities by various laboratories on the grounds that their approach is too academic; that their conception of industry is a "caricature"; or, more generally, that, having a broad, long-range program of their own, they are unlikely to give to a designated development task the concentrated effort needed for its timely success. As one executive summed up the views of many in the reactor industry, to give the labs a stronger role "will hold up development of an economic industry."

Non-Nuclear Work

The multi-program laboratories have made periodic efforts, sometimes against the wishes of the Commission, to broaden and diversify the range of their activities by pushing into related investigations of an applied or basic scientific nature, and, of late, even by conducting non-nuclear work. While we will dwell on the latter method here, it is merely an extension of the former, which has substantially enlarged the content of the nuclear domain. This has been a natural enough process, in view of scientists' instincts to explore the entire realm of knowledge and the practical need for knowledge in a wide range of fields to overcome the extraordinary technical problems of reliably and economically controlling nuclear reactions. "You can use a shovel for atomic energy; in fact

---

[48] Commissioner Robert Wilson in *ibid.*, p. 465.

you do. You can use a bottle of beer for atomic energy. In fact you do," J. Robert Oppenheimer observed in 1949,[49] and the scope of atomic energy has not diminished since. All sorts of shovels and bottles—tools to measure and manipulate, and containers of novel materials and configurations—have been developed in the process.

Nevertheless, as one advocate of a larger role for the multi-program laboratories put it, "The problems of atomic energy are broad but finite. What do you do with these institutions when their mission is accomplished?" Two main answers can be given: close down the laboratory, in whole or in part, disposing of the property either to the highest bidder or, preferably, to that bidder (public or private) who proposes to use it for a purpose adjudged to be in the best interest of the public; or broaden the laboratory mission to include important non-nuclear work. These answers are not mutually exclusive, for it may be desirable to close down or cut back some laboratories and to broaden the mission of others.

Cutbacks are difficult enough to achieve,[50] but the more drastic alternative of closing a government laboratory appears virtually impossible for the government to adopt.[51] In June 1960, the AEC General Advisory Committee valiantly declared:

We would not expect that the project engineering laboratories, with the exception of Sandia, would indefinitely have support from and be under the supervision of AEC. In the main these laboratories were established to accomplish specific applied research and development missions. It would appear that when these laboratories have accomplished their missions these installations would be either:

[49] *Investigation into the United States Atomic Energy Project*, Hearings before the Joint Committee on Atomic Energy, 81 Cong. 1 sess. (1949), Pt. 7, p. 282. Oppenheimer was discussing the difficulties of security control and classification in nuclear matters, but his point is, we believe, also appropriate in the present context.

[50] Herman Kahn remarks that reactor programs are never eliminated; they only change their name. A fiendish method of enforcing budgetary cuts, attributed to President Coolidge, is to make raises conditional upon a reduction in total expenditures.

[51] Indeed, the government is so deficient in this skill, it might well recruit a number of generals with demobilization experience, senior Budget Bureau officials, referees in bankruptcy, and statesmen of the former British Empire under the leadership of Defense Secretary Robert McNamara to train science agency executives and congressmen from the affected districts in modern methods of detecting and dismantling unnecessary laboratories.

(1) Transferred to other Government agencies or departments, or

(2) Transferred to industry, or

(3) Reduced in size and eventually discontinued.[52]

However, after the main work of two of these five "project engineering" laboratories[53]—at Evendale, Ohio, and Middletown, Conn.—was cancelled in March 1961, following President Kennedy's message to the Congress recommending termination of the nuclear aircraft propulsion development program,[54] the laboratories continued other nuclear and high temperature materials research. By fiscal year 1963, operating costs at Evendale had fallen to $8.7 million from a level of $37.7 million in 1960, but at Middletown they had risen to $23.4 million from $17.5 million in 1960; not until 1965 was work at the latter site stopped (it was then transferred to Livermore).

With respect to the two "production plant" laboratories at Hanford and Savannah River, the AEC's 1960 report stated that "The primary mission of the production plant laboratories is the improvement of processes at major . . . production centers." It was anticipated that a "decline in production plant support needs . . . should free some facilities and talent" which might be utilized in other work for which the laboratory was qualified. But the Commission expressly stated that it "does not plan to develop these facilities as multiprogram laboratories," signifying that their programs would be kept narrower than those of the multi-program laboratories; and implying that the Commission did not feel the same moral compulsion to maintain their budgetary level (or, as it has often been put more romantically, "vitality") as it did that of

[52] In *The Future Role of the Atomic Energy Commission Laboratories, op. cit.,* p. 244.

[53] At Evendale (the Aircraft Nuclear Propulsion Facility), Middletown (the Connecticut Aircraft Nuclear Engine Laboratory), Pittsburgh (Bettis Laboratory), Schenectady (Knolls Atomic Power Laboratory), and Albuquerque (Sandia Laboratory).

[54] Over $1 billion was spent by the Air Force and the AEC on the aircraft nuclear propulsion program from 1946 to 1961. The scarcely credible story of repeated efforts by the President and the Secretary of Defense to terminate or redirect the program, which flared up again and again in Air Force and AEC contract facilities, is recounted in *Report to the Congress of the United States, Review of Manned Aircraft Nuclear Propulsion Program, Atomic Energy Commission and Department of Defense,* Comptroller General of the United States, February 1963.

the multi-program laboratories. The Commission also declared
". . . there is no intention to assign them tasks that can more appropriately be performed in private facilities, . . ."[55]

However, once Hanford actually confronted the long-feared crisis in January 1964, when President Johnson announced that
three of the nine plutonium production reactors on the reserva-
tion would be shut down, eliminating 2,000 positions by June
1965,[56] the Commission took a different tack. It now argued that
the laboratory was a national resource whose staff and equipment
should be utilized by public and private interests for non-nuclear
work insofar as they were not needed for nuclear tasks. Now the
versatility of the Hanford laboratory and its usefulness for varied
scientific and industrial purposes was stressed. One private observer who foresaw great opportunities for the erstwhile "production" laboratory in fields of civilian technology asserted that 85

[55] The full statements on the functions of the production plant laboratories were
as follows:

"The primary mission of the production plant laboratories is the improvement of
processes at major Commission production centers. They will continue to be needed
to support the production facilities which they serve. The Commission does not
plan to develop these facilities as multiprogram laboratories; however, the Commission intends to continue to utilize the talents and facilities of these laboratories
in support of its reactor development and biology and medicine programs. Such use
will be secondary to their production support missions.

"The anticipated decline in production plant support needs at the Hanford and
Savannah River Laboratories should free some facilities and talent for other work.
Within Commission programs, such assignments are most likely to be in the nuclear
technology field. As new tasks need to be undertaken, the capabilities of these
laboratories will be carefully assessed, particularly if such assignments would otherwise call for expanding Government facilities elsewhere, or expanding the personnel
of another Commission laboratory. But there is no intention to assign them tasks
that can more appropriately be performed in private facilities, or to transfer going
activities from other laboratories; 'make work' tasks will not be resorted to as a
means of maintaining the vitality of these institutions." The Future Role . . . ,
op. cit., pp. 12 and 33, respectively.

[56] In December 1965, it was estimated that slightly over 1,000 positions had been
eliminated due to the shutdown of the three Hanford production reactors, and an
additional 150 would be eliminated when the separations plant was shut down at
the end of June 1966. "However, only 200 layoffs have had to be issued because of
the job placement programs initiated by the General Electric Company and the
Atomic Energy Commission, together with attrition and people taking advantage of
early retirement opportunities" (Dec. 14, 1965 letter from Clarence Ohlke, Director,
AEC Office of Economic Impact and Conversion).

percent of the laboratory's activities "had nothing to do" with the production works. An energetic pursuit of research and development work for other government agencies was undertaken; already in 1963, the AEC had arranged for visits to Hanford by senior Department of Defense and National Aeronautics and Space Administration officials, and NASA has assigned to Hanford several tasks concerned with tungsten-uranium fuel element development estimated to cost $1.6 million. Additional AEC research and development expenditures at Hanford created over 300 new jobs by December 1965.[57]

As of late 1965, it appeared that the Commission had not resolved what its policy toward the Hanford laboratory (now renamed the Pacific Northwest Laboratory) would be. Some AEC staff believed that the diversification would occur only in activities the laboratory undertook for other government agencies and for private clients, and that the Commission had not altered its earlier conception of the laboratory or the range of nuclear programs it would put there. Others believed that a significant change had occurred, and that Hanford had advanced substantially toward the status of a "multi-program" laboratory. In 1965, they noted, the laboratory was doing considerable work for the reactor, research and biology divisions, whereas a decade earlier, it had been confined mainly to work for the production division.

It remains to be seen what will happen to the laboratory when the new five year AEC management contract with the Battelle Memorial Institute has run its course in December 1969. The Commission will have done nobly if it can gradually cut back its expenditures while maintaining or expanding total laboratory operations by encouraging Battelle to take on R&D for other government and private sponsors. For it will have demonstrated two things: that even a rather specialized nuclear laboratory is convertible to non-nuclear tasks; and that a government agency can extricate itself honorably and at something better than a giveaway price from a major investment in a laboratory.

In earlier years, when its mission and budget were expanding, the AEC was more inclined to discourage laboratories from under-

[57] *Ibid.*

taking non-nuclear work for other agencies. Thus, in 1951, Associated Universities, Inc. obtained an amendment to its Brookhaven contract permitting use of the laboratory facilities and personnel for other governmental or private agencies, with a corresponding reduction in costs charged to the contract, provided prior AEC permission was received. AUI thereupon undertook, among other work, Project East River, a study of civil and military measures for the Federal Civil Defense Administration and the Department of Defense; research for the General Electric Company; a study of radio astronomy needs for the National Science Foundation that subsequently led AUI into the management of the National Radio Astronomy Observatory at Green Bank, W. Va.; and a good deal of meteorological research for the Air Force. However, except for its responsibilities at Green Bank, this work was usually short-lived and did not bulk large in the continuing laboratory programs. AUI recognized "that the Commission under its present policy would not countenance any use of the site or the Laboratory staff that seemed likely to divert the aims of the Laboratory or to endanger its continuity and homogeneity. With this policy the corporation is in full agreement."[58]

Today the outlook is changing. The Oak Ridge Institute of Nuclear Studies has been reconstituted as the Oak Ridge Associated Universities (with ORINS as its major subsidiary unit) to

... broaden the opportunity for member institutions collectively to participate in many fields of education and research beyond those related to nuclear energy. ... It is not only conceivable but probable that in the future opportunities will arise for administering programs unrelated to nuclear studies.[59]

The newly formed Universities Research Association, established in 1965 with an eye to managing the construction and operation of the prospective 200-bev accelerator, proposes, in due course, to offer its services to other government agencies for the operation of

[58] Associated Universities, *Report of Associated Universities, Inc.*, New York, January 1952-July 1953, p. 38; see also Associated Universities, *Report of the President to the Board of Trustees* (Dec. 31, 1951), pp. 9-10, 13, and 21-22.

[59] Statement of Dr. Paul M. Gross, president of ORINS, in a press release issued by ORINS March 3, 1965. ORINS has already undertaken a study of southern manpower training resources and needs for the Department of Labor.

other national scientific facilities and programs.[60] Laboratories accustomed for two decades to continual expansion cannot readily accept the prospect of stable, or, in some areas, declining budgets with an accompanying loss of morale and the departure of more enterprising staff.[61] Yet the Commission's operating and capital expenditures for R&D peaked in 1965 at $1,520 million after an uninterrupted and usually generous rise each year since 1947, and were expected to decline slightly in both 1966 and 1967, reductions having been projected for the AEC's two largest R&D programs, on reactors and on special nuclear materials and weapons.[62] The mounting appropriations for high energy physics have been questioned, though not yet denied, by Congress.

In view of the increased laboratory interest in undertaking research and development for other government agencies, the Commission, in March 1964, issued policy and procedure guidelines for such work. Proposals to perform non-nuclear work for other agencies, it was announced, would be considered "on a case-by-case basis" provided:

1. The proposed work will not result in an increase in the size of AEC or contractor staff.

2. The proposed work will not require additions of new AEC facilities

[60] See "URAI Board of Trustees Elects Officers, Trustees-at-Large," *News Report,* National Academy of Sciences (December 1965), p. 3. One possible candidate for URAI management that was cited before Congress put at least a temporary end to the project in 1966 was the National Science Foundation's Mohole drilling program.

[61] This strikes us as a moderate formulation of the general outlook of AEC (and many other) laboratories, and a great deal of evidence could be adduced to substantiate it. However, the thesis is not universally accepted within the AEC, and, in the course of time and persistently recalcitrant budgets, a more homeostatic conception of the laboratory may well emerge.

The director of one of the most dynamic AEC laboratories rejected the thesis explicitly. In his view, his laboratory had outgrown the idea that it must constantly expand. "We're building a capability . . . if the nation doesn't need it, that's fine." The lab, he declared, would never seek to protect the size of its budget, staff, or facilities just for their own sake. When, in 1965, the phasing out of a successful development program led to a staff reduction of 150 men, "we felt it was an opportunity." It was fruitless to push a program which was not inherently important and exciting. "It is a terrible mistake to try and keep a dying horse alive. . . ,"

It does not, of course, follow that his laboratory has been incapable of initiating technically significant, attractive, and expensive ideas.

[62] See Special Analysis I, "Federal Research, Development, and Related Programs," *Budget of the United States, 1967,* p. 122.

or modifications to existing facilities solely to place AEC in a position to supply or render the requisitioned services.

3. The proposed work may not be subcontracted, except for work requisitioned by agencies specifically designated in the Economy Act.

4. The Government agency requesting such work has determined that the work cannot be as conveniently or more cheaply performed by private industry. The receipt of the request will ordinarily be construed that the other agency has made such a determination.

In deciding whether or not to approve work for other agencies, AEC and laboratory staff were cautioned, the Commission would take into consideration that:

1. . . . other agencies do not assume the same sense of responsibility to maintain a stable level of effort at an AEC facility as does the AEC. . . .

2. Highly qualified staff members working on AEC programs may become so heavily engaged in work for other agencies, that, as a result, the quality of the AEC research and development program may be adversely affected.

3. Situations may arise where, because of heavy work schedules, priorities, facility or equipment usage, certain AEC work could not be performed on a timely basis despite prior planning to the contrary.

4. AEC intends that as a general rule work for other agencies will be performed when it is important in the national interest and the AEC facility has unique or close to unique capabilities for carrying it out, and that our facilities will not become "job shops."

The foregoing considerations may be balanced by possible benefits which diversification of a particular operation may have in tending to reduce economic impact due to actual or anticipated cutbacks in AEC programs.[63]

The laboratory that has proceeded furthest in its work for other agencies is Oak Ridge. About $5.5 million or 7 percent of the Oak Ridge budget in 1964 represented nuclear-related[64] R&D for the Department of Defense and NASA and non-nuclear research for

[63] From "Research and Development Work for Other Government Agencies," memorandum from Assistant General Manager for Research and Development to Managers of Field Offices and Heads of Divisions and Offices, HQ, April 28, 1964.

[64] "I would like to see a clear definition of that: sort of like 'kissing-cousins down South,' I expect," observed an irreverent industry reader.

the Interior Department, the Public Health Service, and the Office of Civil Defense. One observer commented that, given its own head, the laboratory might at times prefer to drop some lines of nuclear work as being of less national importance or technical promise than the non-nuclear work, but, as the Commission was less likely to sanction that, the usual consequence was a net addition of non-nuclear work to its existing programs. The work for Interior's Office of Saline Water Conversion involved basic research on the chemical properties of water and the technology of materials in aqueous solutions, an outgrowth of the laboratory's research in the chemical processing, purification, and decontamination of aqueous solutions. For the Public Health Service, Oak Ridge was investigating the role of radiation, viruses, and chemicals as causes of cancer, an extension of its long-standing work on radiation effects and treatment, and on ultra-high speed centrifuges; the entire program in biology has been characterized as research on "physical insults to the biosphere." For the Office of Civil Defense, the laboratory has instituted a program of research in civil defense under the leadership of Eugene Wigner.

Glenn Seaborg suggested in 1961 that the AEC laboratories "could well advance the national interest by doing work on: long-range transmission of electricity; better control over environmental pollution; long-range prediction and control of weather; . . . exploitation of ocean minerals; biophysics and biochemistry; and national resources."[65] More recently, an AEC staff study has added that Oak Ridge or Hanford might conduct "water research programs for the Department of Health, Education and Welfare, space research . . . for NASA, coal research . . . for the Department of the Interior, and a design center for the Corps of Engineers."[66] Some enthusiasts envisage that by 1970 as much as half, or $50 million of a then $100 million Oak Ridge budget, might go into non-nuclear work.

Oak Ridge's concerted move into non-nuclear fields began in

[65] Report of address by Seaborg to American Physical Society, April 1961, in *Nucleonics* (July 1961), p. 26.

[66] "Report on AEC Cooperation in Industrial Development Efforts of Communities Such as Richland, Washington, and Oak Ridge, Tennessee" (multilithed), early 1964, p. 9.

1961 when laboratory director Alvin Weinberg asked permission to embark on a substantial program of work on the desalination of salt water.

His request was particularly timely because it was tendered as: 1. officials of the new Administration—particularly President Kennedy and AEC Chairman Glenn T. Seaborg—were giving their support to the use of national-laboratory resources for public-interest projects outside the nuclear field. . . . 2. the labs were feeling pressure from both reduced budgets and the continuing industrial campaign to get AEC-funded work industry is capable of handling . . . and 3. the nation, as a whole, was taking a greater interest in future water resources.[67]

The National Association of Manufacturers' (NAM) nuclear energy committee regarded this proposal as posing a sufficiently significant policy departure to visit the Commission in January 1962 and register a protest, which was, however, received with some coolness. According to reports, one AEC commissioner read to the committee passages from the AEC's 1960 report extolling the laboratories as national assets. Another stated that, as time went on and the needs of the atomic energy program might well lessen, the resources and staff of laboratories like Oak Ridge should be made available for other jobs of national importance; the Commission did not, however, expect to expand the laboratories by this means; non-nuclear programs would be introduced by substitution, not expansion. Two months later, the Commission formally approved the desalination program; and the NAM did not contest Oak Ridge's subsequent entry into cancer and civil defense work.

As an essentially promotional body which has prided itself on pushing the more deliberative Commission into repeated program expansions, the Joint Committee on Atomic Energy has viewed with favor these efforts to diversify the multi-program laboratories. Committee members, many of whom come from states with AEC installations or high fuel costs, have not been inclined to break up the laboratories and have defended them against industry charges of "unfair competition." In response to the detailed bill of

[67] *Nucleonics* (August 1961), p. 30.

particulars about laboratory "competition" drawn up in February 1960 by the Chamber of Commerce and the NAM Committee Chairman Senator Clinton Anderson "let it be known that he is against providing a sounding board for industry complaints that the labs and other AEC-owned facilities are competing with industry. Anderson and other JCAE leaders have little sympathy with the industry attacks . . . because they feel the labs should be preserved as important research-and-development centers."[68] No doubt the Joint Committee has preferred to see the laboratories used to capacity in nuclear work,[69] but a committee which once aspired to jurisdiction over the space program[70] was not inclined to reject a broader charter for the laboratories. The key question is: can the laboratories, the AEC, and the Joint Committee *get* a broader charter from the Administration and the Congress?

While it is too early to answer this question, it is not too early to raise it. Until 1964, expenditures on weapons R&D and fabrication, and that portion of its ore procurement and nuclear materials production allocable to military purposes dominated the AEC budget. However, commencing in the early 1960's, this emphasis began to change noticeably. It is true, the line for "weapons de-

[68] *Nucleonics Week* (Feb. 11, 1960), p. 1.
[69] Cf. Congressman Melvin Price, chairman of the Joint Committee's Subcommittee on Research, Development, and Radiation: "We have found . . . that advanced reactor physics work, reactor material development work and liquid metal experimental work for reactor systems is being carried out by NASA. . . . Atomic Energy Commission laboratories were set up to perform just such work. . . . The responsibility for inadequate utilization of available facilities . . . lies with the AEC . . . before non-nuclear work is assigned to Commission laboratories, every effort should first be made to fully utilize the nuclear development potential of these facilities." "Pre-countdown Problems in the Nuclear Space Program," remarks before Princeton University Conference on Prospects for Nuclear Aerospace Propulsion (Feb. 15, 1962).
[70] "At the end of January, 1958, Anderson led the Committee's brief, abortive drive to win jurisdiction of outer space, including the missile program. Anderson, Gore, Durham, and Holifield introduced bills amending the Atomic Energy Act to provide for outer-space development by the AEC. They maintained that the facilities already available to the AEC—the network of national laboratories staffed with excellent scientists—could not be duplicated easily and that there was no necessity to create an additional agency to undertake the task. . . . Since passage of the National Aeronautics and Space Act of 1958, the JCAE and the space committees have been engaged in intermittent conflict over their respective roles." Harold Green and Alan Rosenthal, *Government of the Atom* (1963), pp. 218-19.

velopment and fabrication" in the Commission's financial reports climbed every postwar year but one, that is on record, to an all-time high of $805 million in 1964; but weapons development and testing have since been stabilized,[71] while weapons manufacture has been cut. The latter cut, first announced by President Johnson in June 1964 but evidently initiated in 1962,[72] led to a reduction of some 3,555 positions or 13 percent of total employment in AEC weapons production plants during 1965 alone.[73] Expenditures on uranium ore have declined steeply since 1961, and on the production of nuclear materials (an increasing amount of which goes for civilian reactors), more gradually, since 1962.

In the single year from 1964 to 1965, the conjuncture of these factors led to a dramatic drop of $524 million or 29 percent in AEC expenditures allocable to military purposes (Table 11). The resultant budgetary slack has been absorbed mainly by the expansion of R&D in civilian nuclear science and technology, and it is not too much to say that, within a year, the AEC was transformed from an agency with primarily military objectives, to one in which civilian and military goals now receive equal budgetary weight.[74]

In addition to their expansion of R&D in civilian nuclear fields, some AEC laboratories have undertaken (and others have contemplated) a relatively small but growing volume of non-nuclear

[71] The following elements of the weapons programs "will remain approximately at the 1966 level [during FY 1967] . . . : (1) the development of improved weapon designs; (2) the conduct of underground weapons testing; and (3) the program, conducted jointly with the Department of Defense, to maintain a readiness for resumption of atmospheric testing. . . ." (*The Budget of the United States Government Fiscal Year Ending June 30, 1967*, p. 83).

[72] "Already we have cut back on production of atomic fuel and weapons," President Johnson remarked in the course of a talk at Minneapolis on June 28, 1964 (see *Public Papers of the Presidents . . . Lyndon B. Johnson, 1963-64*, Book I, p. 831). According to the *New York Times*, this statement "represented the first official disclosure that the production of atomic weapons was declining after 15 years of steadily increasing output. . . .

"The cutback apparently began over two years ago. . . ." John F. Finney, "A.E.C. Affirms Cut In Output of Arms," *New York Times* (Aug. 26, 1964), pp. 1, 29.

[73] See AEC *Annual Report for 1965*, pp. 45 and 97.

[74] To be sure, budgets are not the only test of an agency's goals. Not only may its history still incline the AEC to give greater priority to military goals; its statute enjoins it to do so. Sec. 1(a) of the 1954 Atomic Energy Act declares that the Commission's other work shall be "subject at all times to the paramount objective of making the maximum contribution to the common defense and security."

TABLE 11

AEC Expenditures for Military and Civilian Purposes, 1951–65[a]

(Dollar amounts in millions)

Year	Expenditures			Percent civilian
	Total	Military	Civilian	
1965	$2624	$1331	$1293	49
1964	2765	1855	910	33
1963	2758	1944	814	30
1962	2806	2038	768	27
1961	2713	2048	665	25
1960	2623	2044	579	23
1959	2541	2017	524	21
1958	2268	1910	358	16
1957	1990	1629	361	18
1956	1651	1408	243	15
1955	1857	1694	163	9
1954	1895	1823	72	4
1953	1791	1631	160	9
1952	1670	1435	235	14
1951	897	681	216	24

Sources: *Report of the Committee on Economic Impact of Defense and Disarmament*, Gardner Ackley, chairman (July 1965), p. 76, and Atomic Energy Commission.
[a] Fiscal years.

R&D for other government agencies, which has posed significant policy issues. R&D projects assigned to AEC facilities by other government agencies do not usually enjoy the same priority or budgetary stability as projects assigned to their own facilities or to contractors in their normal entourage. And the projects must be justified before congressional committees less familiar with, and less committed to, the AEC laboratories than the avuncular Joint Committee. Legally, there is some doubt about how far the Commission can go, under existing statutes, in sanctioning—let alone encouraging—non-nuclear work in its facilities. Sec. 33 of the Atomic Energy Act of 1954 provides that, "Where the Commission finds private facilities or laboratories are inadequate to the purpose, it is authorized to conduct for other persons, through its own facilities, such of those activities and studies . . . as it deems *appropriate to the development of atomic energy* [our italics]."

Indeed, there is some question whether, under the terms of this Act, it is lawful for the Commission to conduct non-nuclear work in its laboratories.[75]

The Commission has sought to avoid the legal issue by justifying this work as a "service" rendered under the Economy Act[76] which provides that, where work can thus be performed more cheaply, one agency can render a service to another agency at cost, if facilities and staff are available.[77] And it has sought to avoid the large issues of public policy involved by considering each proposal to conduct non-nuclear work on an ad hoc basis. Were a broader authorization of non-nuclear work contemplated, one AEC informant suggested, either special legislation or special approval from the Joint Committee should first be obtained. Each proposal to do work for another agency is, in any event, approved by Congress through the normal authorization and budgetary process and, he added, AEC's statutory authority is already so broad that "it is hard to find work that is *not* peripherally related to nuclear work."[78] An ad hoc approach combines a maximum of flexibility

[75] Thus, at a forum of the Federal Bar Association convention in the Sheraton Hotel, Philadelphia, Sept. 25, 1963, Neil Naiden, former AEC counsel, questioned the legality of the Commission's conducting NASA work at Hanford under the terms of the 1954 Act. (This does not mean, of course, that the Commission is operating illegally, since its work for other government agencies clearly has a variety of legal sanctions, including the Economy Act and authorization acts of the Joint Committee and of the Congressional committees responsible for the agencies concerned.)

[76] Title 31, U. S. Code 686, June 30, 1932, states that "Any executive department or independent establishment of the Government . . . if it is determined by the head of such executive department . . . to be in the interest of the Government so to do, may place orders with any other such department . . . for . . . work, or services, of any kind that such requisitioned Federal agency may be . . . equipped to render. . . . *Provided* . . . That if such work or services can be as conveniently or more cheaply performed by private agencies such work shall be let by competitive bids to such private agencies."

[77] In at least one instance, an AEC official stated, ". . . we weren't completely equipped and [the laboratory] had to hire a few new people." A minor amount of hiring or remodeling is evidently compatible with the terms of the Economy Act.

[78] Cf. the observation of the National Academy of Sciences Panel on Basic Chemical Research in Government Laboratories chaired by Joseph Kratz of Argonne: "The chemical aspects of nuclear energy are so broad that most areas of chemical research, but by no means all, fall within the scope of Section 31 (of the 1954 Atomic Energy Act)." *Basic Chemical Research in Government Laboratories*, Publication 1292-A, National Academy of Sciences (1966), p. 49, footnote.

with a minimum of political jeopardy; it is also an excellent (or, some may feel, a poor) substitute for confronting a significant policy issue.

Proponents of a broader role for the AEC laboratories argue that, although three laboratories (Brookhaven, Argonne, and Oak Ridge) preempted the word "national" without any special congressional authorization, all multi-program laboratories now merit the designation. ". . . the only large-scale [development] programs which have been really well done," asserts the Los Alamos laboratory, "have been done by the Government in Government laboratories operated by industrial or academic contractors. Radar, the proximity fuse, and the atomic energy program are conspicuous examples."[79] "Just as for the military protection of our country we have planes 'on flight' at all times, it is equally important that we have strong national laboratories 'on flight' . . . so that they will be available as *going* concerns with the scientific and technological strength to become engaged in any important program, whether it be related to the field of atomic energy or to a number of other fields one can readily imagine as becoming of national importance."[80]

Opponents fear that a broader role for the laboratories may develop before it has been defined or determined to be necessary; and they doubt that it is either necessary or desirable for government laboratories to do what private laboratories could do, even if at greater expense. As W. E. Johnson, General Manager of Hanford operations for General Electric, put the matter presciently in April 1960:

Growth [of AEC laboratories] may . . . occur, perhaps inadvertently, by the laboratories becoming involved in space power systems and other new developments generally associated with the Government's role in promoting research and development in areas related to the exploration of space and of the oceans in addition to work that may be undertaken as a contribution to the national defense. If this should happen in a major degree, the Commission laboratories may, in fact,

[79] In *The Future Role of the Atomic Energy Commission Laboratories, op. cit.,* p. 141.
[80] From an address by Warren C. Johnson on the "Role of Some of the AEC Laboratories," before the American Nuclear Society, Washington, D. C., Nov. 6, 1959.

be converted into Government-owned scientific laboratories with extremely broad charters. The role of the Commission as a sponsor of such laboratories may then be brought into question. I suggest that this aspect of the situation be carefully explored on a continuing basis to determine whether such laboratories under Government ownership are appropriate, and, if so, what agency of the Government properly should be responsible for their administration.[81]

The spectacular achievements of military technology, whose further advances in many fields merely gild the lilies of death, have drawn attention to such spectacular failures of civil technology as traffic jams, slums, and the pollution of air, water, and crops; and if failure were viewed not as malfunction or obsolescence but an inability to compete in world markets, the list could be greatly enlarged. What is the proper role of government, and of government laboratories, in the improvement of civilian technology—particularly, technology that impinges greatly upon the general welfare? Congress has been called upon to define this role in fields as diverse as space exploration, cancer chemotherapy, communication satellites, water desalination, coal utilization, and supersonic air transport. In varied fields of civilian technology, the government has thereby assumed disparate, ad hoc responsibilities exercised by both specially created and long-established agencies in all manner of public and private facilities. Is the time approaching when the Congress should define more broadly the proper function of designated agencies, and of their laboratories, in the realm of civilian technology? If this task is too large, at present, a useful start can be made by defining more precisely the proper function of the AEC and its network of contractor-operated laboratories in non-nuclear science and technology.

[81] In *The Future Role* . . . , *op. cit.,* p. 223.

CHAPTER VI

Contract Administration

Both in spirit and in the humbler particulars of contractual and administrative practice, the heroic days of the Manhattan Project (the days of creation, one is almost inclined to say) contrast strikingly with the increasingly ordinary years that have followed.

The Heroic Days

There was very little formal contract "administration" in the days of the Office of Scientific Research and Development (OSRD) and the Manhattan Project, if that word means carefully drawn regulations under which a group of government employees direct, supervise, and evaluate the work of contractors. Attention was focused on getting the job done, not on costs, controls, and time consuming reports.

At one university heavily involved in the atomic project, the main administrative responsibilities of OSRD were apparently consummated in a review that took a couple of hours and was conducted on the spot twice a year by Conant and two other senior OSRD officers. Decisions were made rapidly, and little attention was paid to the budget. Agreements were often verbal and contractual details were worked out later, sometimes after the work had been completed.

Two classic stories may serve as illustrations. On a visit to St. Louis in May 1942, Arthur Compton told Edward Mallinckrodt, Chairman of the Board of the Mallinckrodt Chemical Works, that

. . . we needed to process sixty tons of uranium. It was impossible to set a price until the processes were worked out in more detail. . . . The only assurance I could give Mallinckrodt was that the Office of Scientific Research and Development would supply him with a letter of intent to work out a contract that would not leave him financially the loser. . . . Some months later, [after the Army had taken over] Colonel K. D. Nichols dropped in at my office. "A. H.," he said, "you'll be interested to know that we have finally signed the contract with Mallinckrodt for processing the first sixty tons of uranium. It was the most unusual situation that I have ever met. The last of the material was shipped from their plant the day before the terms were agreed upon and the contract signed."[1]

Again, in September 1942, Colonel Nichols met in New York with M. Edgar Sengier, managing director of the Belgian Congo Union Minière, who had over 1,200 tons of 65 percent uranium oxide stored in steel drums in a Staten Island warehouse.

When Sengier was assured [that Nichols represented the Army and had authority to buy the ore] . . . he immediately noted on a sheet of yellow paper the conditions of sale of the ore. . . . These notes were dated and initialed by Nichols and Sengier. Within a week the 1200 tons . . . were delivered. . . . It took another six months for the business officers on the two sides to agree upon the form of contract.[2]

"This," General Groves has written, "was typical of the way in which a great many of our most important transactions were carried out. Once the seller understood the importance of our work . . . he was invariably perfectly willing to deliver his goods or his services on our oral assurance that fair terms and conditions would be settled at a later date. We always promised that he would not be out-of-pocket for any expenses incurred if for some reason final agreement was not reached. And we always kept that promise."[3]

Groves did not go in for a large staff. ". . . almost every letter that was ever signed by me during the whole project, was personally written by me. It was not a staff prepared letter. I didn't have a staff in the first place, and I didn't write any letters that weren't

[1] Arthur H. Compton, *Atomic Quest* (Oxford University Press, New York, 1956), pp. 94-95.

[2] *Ibid.*, pp. 96-97.

[3] Leslie Groves, *Now It Can Be Told* (Harper & Bros., New York, 1962), p. 37.

important."[4] "I operated almost entirely on personal oral discussions, either face to face or by telephone. . . . My first office in Washington consisted of two rooms which gradually grew to five. . . . I did not have a Chief of Staff or an Executive Officer. . . . We never did anything ourselves that we could have anyone else do for us. . . . We reasoned that a going organization could do a better job than a newly created one. . . . Every officer knew that delays could not be permitted. Any which he felt would delay the completion of the entire project by as much as twenty-four hours had to be reported to me by telephone."[5] Groves' principal administrative standard can be summed up in one word: speed. "A wrong decision that brought quick results was better than no decision at all. If there were a choice between two methods, one of which was good and the other promising, build both. Time was more important than money . . ."[6] ("A wrong decision that brings results is not a wrong decision," remarked one reader involved in the Manhattan Project. "The best decision not vigorously carried out is not as good as a less good decision vigorously implemented . . .")

This was fine during the war, when each day's delay meant the lives of many American soldiers and even (if the Germans developed the bomb first) the danger of losing the war. But it was not a standard that was normally feasible to maintain in time of peace. It may be noted, however, that the wartime spirit, the sense of having been part of a heroic effort that resulted in a great historic achievement, remains a perceptible bond among veteran participants in the atomic enterprise. To some extent, this spirit was recaptured during the crash program to develop the hydrogen bomb; to some extent in other major new tasks of national importance which dynamic and visionary men have continued to search out. Translated into administrative terms, it means: pushing men hard, working around the clock to achieve a major, clearly defined objective; phoning instead of writing; making decisions on the

[4] Testimony of Groves in *In the Matter of J. Robert Oppenheimer*, Atomic Energy Commission (1954), p. 180.

[5] Leslie Groves, "The A-Bomb Program," in Fremont Kast and James Rosenzweig, eds., *Science, Technology, and Management* (McGraw-Hill, New York, 1963), pp. 39-40 and 37.

[6] Richard G. Hewlett and Oscar E. Anderson, Jr., *The New World, 1939-1946* (Pennsylvania State University Press, University Park, 1962), p. 181.

spot; buying time with money; cutting red tape; and getting the job done.

Slow Centralization Under the Commission

During the almost year and a half that intervened between the end of the war and the transfer of responsibility to the civilian Atomic Energy Commission on January 1, 1947, Groves and the Army officers under his command could, for the most part, take only such actions as were patently necessary to hold the nuclear project together, for broad national policies had first to be debated and defined by the Congress, and then refined and implemented by the five Commissioners.

The infant Commission thereupon confronted severe practical and administrative problems. Physical conditions in the hastily constructed, government-owned atomic towns were bad; the morale of scientists was low; production plants, built on a wartime basis to last a short time, had deteriorated so that breakdowns were threatened. The Commission did not even know precisely what it had inherited from the Army, for it found "No real inventory of fissionable materials or of secret documents;" "we didn't have a set of books showing costs," Lilienthal noted in his diary, "since the Army's Manhattan District didn't have or keep any . . ."[7] The principal contractors had followed different methods of accounting so that comparable financial reporting was impossible; and, in short, the AEC controller Paul Green lamented the "generally unbusiness-like character of the Manhattan District financial records and accounts. . . ."[8]

These were rectified by the introduction in 1948 of a uniform, industry-type accounting system for all major "integrated" con-

---

[7] See statement by Lilienthal in *Investigation into the United States Atomic Energy Project*, Hearings before the Joint Committee on Atomic Energy, 81 Cong. 1 sess. (1949), Pt. 23, p. 1114, and *The Journals of David Lilienthal, op. cit.*, entry for May 25, 1947, Vol. II, p. 181. The accuracy of some of this "Lilienthal version" was disputed by a reader who had been with the Army at the time. ". . . there was an inventory of fissionable materials which stood up pretty well, and that was the only thing we cared about."

[8] See statement by Paul Green, July 11, 1949, in *Investigations into the United States Atomic Energy Project, op. cit.*, p. 1085.

tractors, the term "integrated" meaning that the contractor maintained, for his contract operations, a set of books compatible with
those of the Commission, enabling the Commission to prepare detailed monthly and annual statements of the operating costs and
financial status of the entire national program. In December 1950,
a Procurement Policy Guide was issued, which has been maintained to date and periodically revised as the AEC Procurement
Regulations; like the Armed Services Procurement Regulations,
this amplifies and modifies the standard Federal Procurement
Regulations to meet the agency's special needs and policies.

As has been noted, General Groves had maintained only a small
office in Washington; most Manhattan Project staff had been located at Oak Ridge, with additional offices at Los Alamos, Hanford, and Chicago. At the outset, the distribution of AEC personnel was similar. Of the 4,133 civilian employees on the AEC pay-
roll in May 1947, half were at Oak Ridge and less than 200 in
Washington;[9] but by the latter part of 1958, employment was up
to 5,000, 700 of whom were in Washington.[10]

Under the leadership of Lilienthal, whose TVA background
had led him to champion regional authority, the AEC enunciated
a doctrine of decentralized administration. The Commissioners
were to concern themselves with matters of "high policy" within
which large powers of program implementation and administration were to be delegated to major contractors and to the managers of regional AEC offices (two of whom were paid more than
the Commission chairman). However, the doctrine was gradually
attenuated, because the Commissioners, on the one hand, found
themselves "unable to keep up with the program in sufficient
detail to answer the myriad of questions raised by the Appropriations Committees of both Houses and the Joint Committee. On
the other hand, the officers in the field were not kept abreast of
policy development and so were unable to be very helpful in
melding the many-armed agency into a cohesive, coordinated

---

[9] In addition, the AEC then still had the services of more than 900 officers and
enlisted men. See AEC, *Second Semiannual Report to the Congress* (July 22, 1947),
p. 25.

[10] See *Atomic Energy Development 1947-1948* (Fifth Semiannual Report), Atomic
Energy Commission (1948), p. 140.

program."[11] Division directors who had originally served in a staff capacity were early interposed in the line of authority between the AEC General Manager and field office heads for specific functions, such as the production of feed and fissionable materials, military applications, or reactor development. As the locus of technical competence shifted from the field to headquarters, the influence of regional staff upon program formulation was gradually eroded. When a 1961 reorganization enabled the multi-program laboratories to report directly for overall policy purposes to the newly established Assistant General Manager for Research and Development, Representative Melvin Price observed that

. . . the new reorganization may indicate . . . the relegation of a number of AEC's field offices primarily to the role of auditors and office boys. According to the new organization chart, the operations offices were stripped of any role in implementing programs under Washington direction. If this proves to be the case, then one of the main supports of efficient decentralized administration in AEC will have been badly weakened. The departure of various key officials from AEC field offices in recent months would seem to confirm this trend.[12]

Prior to 1959, the contracting function was handled at headquarters by each cognizant program division. In that year, an Office of Contract Policy (subsequently, the Division of Contracts) was established, centralizing responsibility for the development and issuance of contract policies and for those aspects of contractor selection and negotiation dealt with in Washington. Contract policies and procedures, initially enunciated in ad hoc statements and first codified in the early 1950's, were further formalized by the inception in 1960 of AEC Procurement Regulations implementing and supplementing the Federal Procurement Regulations instituted that year by the General Services Administration. The usefulness of a central contract staff was clear, if only to help resolve conflicting staff recommendations and to coordinate AEC practices with those of other government agencies. One observer suggested,

[11] Arnold Kramish and Eugene Zuckert, *Atomic Energy for Your Business* (David McKay Co., New York, 1956), p. 113.
[12] Melvin Price, "The Nuclear Space Program," in *Atom Forum 1961,* Proceedings of the 1961 Annual Conference of the Atomic Industrial Forum, Atomic Industrial Forum (New York, 1962), p. 19.

however, that it also had certain unfortunate consequences, insofar as it tended to divorce the administration of contracts from the technical objectives they were designed to achieve. In his opinion, the contract was becoming too negative a document, cumbersome and difficult to negotiate, and calculated more to protect the AEC against possible legal disputes than to advance specific program objectives.

While the number and authority of headquarters staff have increased, the bulk of AEC personnel continues to be stationed at offices in the vicinity of major nuclear installations, as indicated by Table 12. There is a noticeable variation in the political strength of different regional offices, the authority exercised by them, and the degree of their rapport with and/or influence upon contractors. The influential area manager enjoys a close relation with Joint Committee members from the area and an intimate and effective working relation with representatives of major (particularly operating) contractors—one which does not rest simply on formal written instructions, but on a mutual understanding and collaboration to achieve common goals. Where such rapport exists, neither contractor nor AEC staff voice significant complaints against the other; both work together harmoniously, locally and in Washington. An area manager referred to one such operating contractor as a "responsive contractor. . . .[He] goes to Washington only when invited, and then we know for what. . . ." By contrast, discontented contractors strive to open or exploit a breach between the local AEC office and headquarters. One contractor managed to get responsibility for the administration of his contract shifted to a different area office; another, whose representative stated that "We talked to the Commissioners . . .[about] how we could liberate ourselves from the clutches of the local AEC people" by reporting more directly to headquarters, apparently failed in that endeavor; a third contractor was said to have "never lost a battle in Washington or won one here [locally]. . . ."

The head of the cognizant field office normally serves as the contract officer whose signature commits the government to the terms of the contract, whose approval is necessary before the contractor incurs costs above a designated amount, and who may direct the contractor to modify the scope or nature of his work.

TABLE 12

Number and Location of AEC Staff, June 30, 1965

Location	Total	Program Direction and Administration	Other Activities[a]
Headquarters	2,133	2,133	—
Operations	1,794	1,794	—
Regulatory functions	339	339	—
Field Offices	4,605	3,255	1,350
Albuquerque	1,424	637	787
Oak Ridge	688	539	149
Idaho Falls	458	214	244
New York	348	238	110
Richland	324	300	24
Chicago	317	311	6
Las Vegas	259	257	2
San Francisco	223	212	11
Savannah River	210	193	17
Grand Junction	146	146	—
Pittsburgh	97	97	—
Schenectady	76	76	—
Brookhaven	35	35	—
Headquarters Field Extensions[b]	309	80	229
Total	7,047	5,468	1,579

Source: Atomic Energy Commission.

[a] Those engaged in direct work operations. At Albuquerque, guards, couriers, and quality inspectors are the principal groups involved; at Idaho Falls, health and safety and radiation monitoring personnel, as well as guards; at Oak Ridge, guards and quality control inspectors; at New York, personnel in two small AEC laboratories referred to in footnote 4, Chapter I.

[b] Extensions of headquarters divisions located in the field. The largest contingent is the staff of the Division of Technical Information stationed at Oak Ridge, which is responsible for the preparation of technical reports and abstracts, microfilms, and a variety of editorial, printing, and publishing activities.

However, as field offices are not usually staffed as strongly with scientific and technical personnel as is headquarters, and are not as well informed about the overall status of the nuclear programs, the AEC has relied increasingly upon program direction from Germantown,[13] leaving to the local staff the function of monitoring compliance and, of course, costs.

[13] Site of the headquarters building some 20 miles northwest of Washington, occupied in 1958 during a periodic effort to disperse some of the government outside of town. It has been found necessary to maintain a second set of offices in town for the Commissioners and key staff.

Proposal Review and Contract Negotiation

The award of small fixed-price contracts by competitive bid (for example, contracts for routine construction or procurement) is handled by a "review board" of regional staff. The award of larger contracts (e.g., as of 1963, construction contracts over $5 million); important operating and cost-plus-fixed-fee contracts in which proposals are invited from a few selected companies or institutions; and any contract involving a significant policy issue must be cleared first with Germantown and may be handled less uniformly. When the award must ultimately be reviewed and approved by Germantown, approval must also be obtained for the criteria and weighting to be used in the selection process, and for the specific form of the "request for proposal" sent to qualified organizations. The evaluation of proposals has then customarily been delegated to a "selection board" of three to five or more persons appointed by the field office manager or, in significant cases, by the director of the AEC Division of Contracts after consultation with AEC program officials.[14] Members of the board, some of whom will be drawn from both field and headquarter staff, have commonly included a lawyer and technically qualified persons. On the few occasions when persons with the requisite technical knowledge cannot be found among government personnel, advisers (who are not, however, members of the selection board and do not make recommendations about particular proposals) may be appointed from the staff of multi-program laboratories or other contractor organizations so placed as to be reasonably neutral for the purpose of the award. Staff of contractor-operated laboratories may also assist in the preparation of technical specifications contained in the request for proposals.

During the last few years, in which the renewal of long-standing operation contracts has been questioned and an effort has been made to "spread the work" among a larger number of contractors,

---

[14] See John Vinciguerra, "Contracting Procedures and Opportunities—AEC Presentation," in *Business Opportunities in the Nuclear Space Program,* Proceedings of the seminar sponsored by the Atomic Industrial Forum and *Nucleonics* (Washington, D. C., Nov. 29, 1962), p. 64.

the AEC Commissioners have themselves reviewed and, upon occasion, set aside the recommendations of selection boards. Thus, in 1961, the Commissioners and the administrator of NASA awarded a space nuclear propulsion contract to two firms which were thus united contractually though they had initially bid competitively. In another case, the Commissioners, troubled about the danger of monopoly, rejected the recommendation of an area selection board that one company (judged the best qualified of those considered during the review process) be awarded an important development contract, choosing instead to break it into several parts each of which was awarded to a different contractor. And in another contract selection, the specifications for an important proposal request were drawn in such a way as to enhance the probability that the contract would go (as, eventually, it did) to a bidder whom an influential member of the nuclear fraternity had earlier sought to interest in the work.

Early in 1965, selection boards were instructed not to prepare numerical ratings of contractors or to make recommendations, but simply to furnish qualitative evaluations in important awards which the Commissioners elected to decide for themselves. Selection boards had always been advisory, the final selection falling to the designating official or the Commissioners, who at times rejected a board's recommendation; and Commissioners had regularly reviewed the award of operating contracts and any other contract over $10 million or which posed a significant policy problem. The new procedure did give Commissioners greater latitude, in implementing the policies of operating contract change and segmentation, to consider matters less susceptible to numerical rating or about which staff were less informed, such as the degree of a firm's interest in the nuclear industry and its probable contribution to industrial diversification or competition. As a result, there was talk about political factors influencing contract awards, which was discounted by AEC spokesmen, one of whom observed that, "The easiest system to fudge is a numerical rating system—it can be the most biased and politically-motivated thing."

Both before and after adoption of the new selection procedure, each contract decision remained an exercise of judgment as to how divergent objectives could best be reconciled in the circumstances of the particular case. Both before and after, the Commission has unquestionably pursued legitimate policy objectives. These objectives have, however, become more complicated lately, and the fact that the Commissioners themselves have had to become so immersed in contract decisions suggests that they have not yet enunciated the overriding policies that govern these awards with sufficient clarity to delegate more of the decisions.

It may also be noted that what is designated as "policy" in the lofty discourse of public administration is politics, economics, and personalities to the individuals involved. This is particularly and inescapably true in the small and semi-closed world of nuclear affairs in which everyone knows (and has opinions about) everyone else, and the actions of the government (i.e., of specific individuals temporarily in seats of public responsibility and accountability) can make or break a nuclear contractor (i.e., specific individuals temporarily in charge of private ventures). "It has been our experience," commented a senior officer of one nuclear company, "that there are too many contracts awarded on the basis of taking care of a particular company or particular group of employees in national laboratories without the prime thought being given to the end result."[15] The AEC would undoubtedly deny this and, in the nature of the case, it is virtually impossible to determine the degree to which such considerations enter into any particular award. For technical objectives, perfectly legitimate economic and political objectives, perfectly normal human objectives, both national policy and specific circumstances, both general ideas and particular men are meshed in the contract process.

The award of lump sum basic research contracts on unsolicited proposals submitted mainly by scientists at universities and nonprofit research institutions is determined by headquarters staff; once the determination has been made, preparation of the contract is handled by staff of the appropriate field office. Headquarter scientists appear to play a larger role in these awards, and particularly in contract renewals, than do those administering comparable basic research grants at the National Science Foundation and

[15] Letter to the Brookings Institution, July 19, 1965.

the National Institutes of Health. Proposals are commonly sent for evaluation by scientists at universities or AEC laboratories,[16] although the AEC does not, like NSF and NIH, maintain standing panels for this purpose. In the case of major and expensive proposals such as those for the construction of high energy accelerators, oral or written comment has been solicited from virtually all of the nation's best qualified scientists, as well as from special ad hoc advisory committees.

Once a prospective contractor has been selected, a period of negotiation commonly ensues between AEC and contractor representatives about the precise terms of the award. On a small research contract, negotiations may be completed during a telephone conversation in which an investigator may be asked if he will accept a sum less than he had requested, the budgetary adjustments he would make, and the date expenditures may start. On a major contract, protracted negotiations may proceed on such matters as the size of the fee, the exact nature of the costs the AEC will meet, the specific conditions under which the work will be regarded as satisfactorily completed, the specific personnel who will direct the project, the extent of liability the AEC will assume, the security provisions that should apply to the site (which has produced some lengthy hassles at large university-managed basic research installations), and so forth. In the area of civilian nuclear power, the Commission is essentially a promotional agency seeking to cajole private and public interests to invest funds in more or less established or experimental types of reactors, and it has a bewildering variety of direct and indirect financial inducements to offer (of which design assistance, R&D contracts, the waiver of a use charge for nuclear materials, and the purchase of plutonium produced by the reactor are only a few), so that it takes considerable wizardry to determine if the terms eventually negotiated for a particular contract are or are not profitable to the contractor. After

[16] Almost all (95 percent or "more than 95 percent" is the way AEC staff put it in December 1965) new proposals received by the Divisions of Research and of Biology and Medicine are sent out for review, normally to two or three scientists at universities and perhaps one or two at AEC laboratories (seldom to a scientist in industry). The Division of Reactor Development has made less use of outside reviewers, relying more on the judgment of staff and advice from the laboratories.

six months of negotiation at a distance and via the local AEC office, the final details of one operating contract for major R&D facilities were agreed upon by senior AEC and contractor staff in three days of face to face discussion at the laboratory, while it took more than a year for Princeton and the Commission to agree to the terms of a large contract for plasma physics research.[17]

The contract is, of course, legally necessary to define the conditions under which public funds may be paid to private persons for a designated purpose, but the document itself is more useful in the event of litigation than in the practical course of day-to-day relations between contractor and government personnel.[18] In a "hands off" buyer-seller relationship, all of the terms that are necessary to the satisfactory completion of a contractual obligation may, perhaps, be put down on paper: the exact goods to be delivered at a given time to a given place for a stated sum. But the most significant aspects of research, development, and managerial contracts are precisely those that cannot be satisfactorily reduced to writing. For they involve the quality of effort made to reach not a precise target but goals that must be continually readjusted by mutual agreement; and—beyond gross and obvious limits—the balance of initiative and responsibility, of freedom and control, that should lie in public and private hands is also a shifting one that must be worked out individually for each major contract. As an early report to the AEC on contract policy wisely put it, ". . . in the course of translating will into motion requests for action cross a bridge from government organization to operating entity. This

[17] See Raymond Woodrow, "Business Arrangements Associated with Federal Programs," in Harrison Sasscer, ed., New Prospects for Achievement, Federal Programs for Colleges and Universities (American Council on Education, Washington, D. C., 1964), p. 52.

[18] Contractual detail provides protection to both the government and the contractor. "This is known as the 'taxicab theory of contract administration,' based upon the invariable speech of a Vice President of a well known university: 'But my dear sir! I know that we understand each other perfectly, and that we will get along splendidly; but if I sign the contract with the present wording, who knows but what a taxicab will run over all of us good people on the way to lunch, and strangers might claim that the words mean other than what you say'"; James T. Ramey and John A. Erlewine, "Introduction to the Concept of the 'Administrative Contract'," in Government Sponsored Research and Development, The Federal Bar Journal (April-June 1957), p. 362, footnote 11.

bridge is the contract—not a piece of paper but a nexus of understanding, imperfectly stated and quite normally more tacit than explicit."[19]

"You work for eight months to get a contract and then you put it in the drawer" remarked the principal administrative officer at a critical AEC facility. Evidently he enjoyed good working relations with AEC staff, as a need to refer constantly to this or that contract clause would evidence poor relations. Clark Center, then general manager of Carbide and Carbon Chemicals' Oak Ridge division, has recorded his misgivings at first examining the Manhattan District contract for operating the K-25 diffusion plant:

My unfamiliarity with contracts led me to believe that such a document was to be followed to the most minute detail. Under such an interpretation my concern became a very real thing. . . . I counted twenty-six . . . sections which required the approval of the Contracting Officer, and, in addition, I learned that the Contracting Officer had the right: ". . . by written order to issue additional instructions, require additional work or services or direct the omission of work or services covered by this contract and that nothing provided in this article excused the Contractor from proceeding with the work so changed. . . ."[20]

Growth of Paperwork

While Center's misgivings were subsequently removed, those of some other contractors have not been, particularly in more recent years. As Lawrence Caruso, legal counsel of the Princeton Office of Research Administration, remarked wryly in 1963, "All administrators seem to suffer from a dread occupational disease, 'administrative ardor,' but the Atomic Energy Commission seems to suffer from it more than other government agencies. . . . The AEC wants to administer and control everything in sight."[21]

Each contractor has his own priority list of grievances at AEC

[19] *Report of Advisory Board on AEC-Contractor Relationships* (the "Loofbourow report"), (Nov. 30, 1947), mimeographed, p. 2.

[20] Clark E. Center, "Progress Toward the Industrialization of Atomic Energy," in *Atomic Energy Industrial and Legal Problems,* University of Michigan Law School, Ann Arbor (1952), p. 127.

[21] Forum discussion at the 1963 convention of the Federal Bar Association, Sheraton Hotel, Philadelphia (Sept. 25, 1963).

contract administration, but one point on many lists is the prior approval required for various expenditures in cost contracts, which can try the patience even of some of AEC's oldest and happiest contractors. Usually, prior approval is required for purchases and subcontracts over a certain amount (which has varied from $5,000 to $100,000, depending upon the time and the contractor). The dollar limit tends to be raised as mutual confidence is established—but confidence is a two-way matter; in some instances the field office has sought to raise the limit, to reduce its workload, while the contractor has preferred to retain it, in order to shift responsibility to the AEC. Approval must also be secured for salaries above a stated amount, for foreign travel (though this was delegated to multi-program laboratory directors in 1961), and certain other expenditures. More important, AEC purchasing regulations are provided to major contractors for guidance in developing their regulations, and contractor procedures and records are reviewed to ensure that they are consistent with AEC policies and needs.

Such controls have aroused little criticism from some operating contractors long accustomed to them and on good terms with field office staff. Other contractors feuding with local staff charged that "guidance" has become virtually mandatory "through the not-so-subtle device of 'No Approval' on procurements unless these [AEC] regulations are followed."

Some criticism has reflected the annoyance of new contractors who, familiar with Department of Defense regulations, disliked having to do things differently for the AEC; and it appears that the Commission has sought to apply to these contractors certain standards derived from more intimate relations with a few long-standing operating contractors. But even contractor representatives with two decades' experience in nuclear affairs have remarked upon the steady growth of controls and paperwork. Some, particularly university contractors, assert that this has had no significant effect upon the vitality of their scientific and technical work, as scientists are shielded from government demands which fall primarily upon administrative staff. Others claim there has been a progressive reduction of the operating contractor's independence, so that he is increasingly obliged to approximate the (it is intimated, sluggardly and uncreative) standards of a conventional government agency. An executive of one major industrial operating contractor expressed this viewpoint forcefully:

[At the outset] contractors were expected to be independent . . . to bring to the government operation the scientific and management skills of industry, their own accounting and business methods, in their negotiations with labor, in subcontracting, in all things characteristic of private industry.

In ensuing years, the independent position of contractors has been largely eroded until they are in fact more like agents than independent contractors. . . . [For example, their] accounting has been lined up with commission practice. The intent is benign, to be consistent and to allow cost comparisons; but the result is not a business system. . . .

We used to do our own procurement; gradually the commission insisted that contractors procure by government methods so they could defend themselves when constituents complained; so we had to open up a bidders list and were denied the opportunity to use our own judgment.

We used to be given an advance which was *our* money; now we draw on a federal account, which is their money, because officials of the federal government are trying to avoid state taxes in federally financed operations.

Another area where we've gone downhill is in labor relations. The commission started by relying on the contractor's self-interest not to negotiate too high labor rates, which would boost the rates in his private plants. During the Truman administration, when they were threatened by a strike at Oak Ridge, they invented the labor panel. . . . This intervention has become a habit, though it is no longer needed to maintain production. . . .

A contractor . . . today is a pseudo-agent, not a truly independent contractor. The large government operations are being run by the government and by government methods, though they get out from under the laws governing procurement and civil service and personnel ceilings.

Virtually no one interviewed during this study disagreed that paperwork and reporting requirements of all sorts had increased in recent years. To document the point, one operating contractor produced the following record of incoming mail from the AEC: in January-May of 1962, 1,022 pieces; during the same months of 1963, 1,419 pieces; and in 1964, 2,118 pieces—mainly from the local AEC office. Senior administrators of one university managing an AEC laboratory exhibited a shelf full of volumes detailing the funds and personnel allocated to every laboratory project, with projections for several years ahead. In contrast to development work which produces tangible hardware, they suggested, there was a tendency to justify the value of intangible research with descriptive and budgetary detail. "You need words to substitute for hardware." But the director of a private company engaged in the development and production of certain nuclear hardware had also noted a marked rise in demands for program detail, which he ascribed to tighter budgets. In 1958 and 1959, he recalled, less detail had been required (a point others confirmed). But, following the inauguration of President Kennedy, cancellation of the aircraft nuclear propulsion program, and the mounting of a major effort to land men on the moon, nuclear programs lost a good deal of their glamour, and increased appropriations went instead to space exploration. Loose controls go with fast development, he observed; tight controls, with a slower pace of development. An officer of a firm managing an AEC laboratory agreed with this analysis: as competition increases, you must make a stronger case to get money; and as nuclear development programs mature, there is more need for central coordination; both factors have led to increased reporting requirements.

"The reports they object to the most are the ones we can't do anything about," said one AEC spokesman who put the onus of responsibility elsewhere—on the General Services Administration, the Small Business Administration, and, above all, the Congress. Particularly since 1960, a contractor executive stated, ". . . the explicit intent of the . . . Joint Committee . . . to obtain greater and considerably more detailed control over the operations of the AEC" has resulted in budgetary delineations and restrictions that have markedly reduced the contractor's flexibility. Others agreed that the request of the Joint Committee and the appropriations committees for program and budgetary detail frequently lay behind the AEC's demand for this information. Lilienthal made the same point years ago: "Congress has more and more tended to assume detailed, item by item control and therefore management of programs which under the Constitution it is the function of the President and his appointees of the executive branch to carry out.

This development has bred delays, dilution of responsibility, mixing of politics into technical matters . . . and general frustration."[22]

But all the blame can by no means be assigned elsewhere. Again and again it was said that the Commission is getting old; bureaucracy builds up as an agency slows down, and the one indispensable commodity for any bureaucracy is paper. "They have a problem with one contractor and they issue a general regulation to cover it, and then they have to explain to other contractors that it doesn't apply to them." It once took three days of his time, a senior laboratory official complained, to get permission for a trivial change in the placement of certain standard building fixtures. "So many controls are being added," an AEC representative acknowledged, "the effectiveness of the contract is being endangered. I'm looking for a successor to the contract." Unfortunately, he did not indicate what that might be.

Who Is Really in Control?

More important than costs is the matter of program, for surely one of the most important questions that can be asked about the AEC's contractual operations is: Have they been directed to public or private objectives? Have public or private interests ultimately been in control?

To so broad a question, an equally broad answer must be given: the objectives have been public, and determined by the proper public authorities (including not only the AEC and the Congress but, as necessary in programs of such moment, the President and his advisers, and the National Security Council). It is true that private citizens, rather than civil servants, have originated most of the

[22] David Lilienthal, *This I Do Believe* (Harper & Bros., New York, 1949), p. 134. A good example can be found in the 1950 report of the House Appropriations Committee: "During hearings . . . it developed that the members of the Commission were not well informed as to the finances of the agency. It was apparent that the people in the field made their own decisions without much control or advice from the Commission. The committee is of the opinion that this is a very unsound way of doing business, that the Commission should have a better knowledge of these affairs and the committee will expect better information from it in that connection during consideration of the 1952 budget." *Report to Accompany H. R. 7786, Independent Offices Appropriations Bill, 1951*, H. Rept. 1797, 81 Cong. 2 sess. (March 3, 1950), p. 202.

technical ideas implemented by the AEC; one could hardly expect otherwise in an endeavor that originated in university laboratories and is still conducted primarily by private organizations (albeit organizations whose nuclear activities are financed largely by the government). Private citizens have also originated a host of technical ideas that, failing the tests of public merit and/or political acceptability, have been discarded by the AEC. There has been little to suggest that public officials have been suborned to private purposes that have not at the same time been defined by the government as national purposes.

This is not to assert that—as judged after the fact—there has been no waste or misdirected effort. The prodigious expenditures of the Manhattan Project, in which four different ways of producing fissionable material were pursued simultaneously to enhance the chances that one, at least, would work, were deliberate and calculated.

. . . the Manhattan Engineer District spent more than $300,000,000 in hastily constructing two major plants for the isotopic separation of U-235 from normal uranium. One plant (known as Y-12 and exploring the electromagnetic principle) operated about 2½ years, whereupon efficiency dictated that it be placed in permanent stand-by except for small-scale activities. The other (known as S-50 and exploiting the thermal diffusion principle) operated only a few months and then proved to be so uneconomical that it was placed in stand-by and finally dismantled altogether.[23]

A visible technical generosity, possible only for an agency well financed by the Congress, persisted under the Commission. Promi-

[23] *Investigation into the United States Atomic Energy Commission,* Joint Committee on Atomic Energy, S. Rept. 1169, 81 Cong. 1 sess. (Oct. 13, 1949), p. 10. On the positive side of these ventures, one informed reader states, "The Y-12 was responsible for the bomb that won the war. The design of the plutonium bomb was set ahead a year by reason of the experimental samples of U-235 obtained from the plant." Adoption of the thermal diffusion process by the Manhattan District was delayed due to a lack of information about it (as the work was going on at the Naval Research Laboratory), and the belief that a product of 100 percent purity was necessary, which would have rendered the process inordinately expensive. S-50 was built when it was realized that thermal diffusion could advantageously be used to bring the feed material up to a lesser degree of purity for further refinement in the gaseous diffusion plants. The new thermal process saved four days in the production of the initial critical quantity of fissionable bomb material.

nent examples include: the opening of a second weapons laboratory and the operation of vigorous, competitive weapons development and testing programs by Livermore and Los Alamos; the construction of additional diffusion plants and plutonium production reactors as well as the continuance of major programs of process improvement at existing plants; the stockpiling of large reserves of uranium ore, fissionable material, and nuclear weapons; the support of varied approaches to controlled hydrogen fusion; the multiplication of accelerators; the pursuit of two major approaches to the development of a nuclear reactor for aircraft propulsion; the conduct of some reactor research and development by almost every major AEC laboratory; and the effort, at one time or another, to develop virtually every conceivable kind of reactor[24]—Commissioner John Floberg once remarked that the only kind the AEC had not tried to design or develop was "a beer-cooled, sawdust-moderated reactor."[25] However, most of this prodigality has been endorsed by the Commission and the Congress to achieve designated objectives rapidly. When an objective has either been achieved (e.g., the nuclear stockpile) or reservations have been expressed about its urgency (e.g., research on controlled hydrogen fusion), expenditures have usually been curtailed and the range of effort correspondingly restricted.

The difficult but critical questions remain: Has the AEC known what has been going on in its contractual empire? Has it adequately monitored the technical status of contractor programs and been able to redirect them, as necessary, to prescribed objectives? In turn, have contractors kept the Commission adequately informed about the status of their work, and have they been sufficiently responsive to direction by the government?

A single, simple answer cannot satisfactorily cover the great range of practices and, indeed, philosophies that have characterized the management of different programs.

At one extreme of tight technical control lies a program such as

[24] "About 1,000 different reactors," counters a reader. "Serious work on about a dozen."

[25] See address by Commissioner Robert Wilson in *AEC Authorizing Legislation Fiscal Year 1965*, Hearings before the Joint Committee on Atomic Energy, 88 Cong. 2 sess. (1964), Pt. 2, p. 1059.

the development of reactors for the propulsion of submarines and other naval vessels, directed by Admiral Rickover, in which technical specifications and time schedules of exacting detail have been prepared, and inspectors have been posted in contractor facilities to monitor the work and test the quality of the product. Comparable controls have been maintained in the production of fissionable materials (in which the Commission has set the production goals and the volume of power, and supplied feed materials to the contractor) and of nuclear weapons (in which virtually every component is numbered and can be traced forward throughout the production process to the finished bomb assembly, or backward from the Mediterranean seabed to its originating subcontractor).

At the other extreme, in the programs of basic research by university scientists, technical control has been entirely absent: essentially the only technical control in these programs has been the evaluation of the quality of the scientist and of his proposed work before a contract award or extension. The large programs of pure research at AEC installations at Cambridge, Brookhaven, Princeton, Oak Ridge, Argonne, Ames, Berkeley, and Stanford have also been basically self-directed by scientists at the laboratory and in affiliated user groups. AEC (and laboratory) staff have been alert to the judgment of eminent scientists about the quality of the research; and have at times striven to confine it to areas more or less relevant to Commission interests or, occasionally, to stimulate work in a relevant but neglected field. Beyond that, little effort has been made to influence the direction of the work.

In between, and perhaps most characteristic of AEC management philosophy, fall the multi-program laboratories and large R&D contracts with industry, in which great responsibility has been delegated to the contractor, and particularly to the laboratory director, although the AEC may, of course, direct such changes in the program as become warranted. "One of the essential characteristics of the relationship between AEC and the contractors . . .," declared a memorandum sent to prospective bidders for an operating contract at Hanford, "is the right and responsibility of the AEC to exercise program direction, surveillance and control over the operations in such detail and at such times as AEC deems desirable. The contractor is expected to work in close day-to-day cooperation with the AEC."[26] In practice, program direction of major R&D contractors has been more sporadic than this statement might lead one to expect. The principal objectives, schedule, and budgetary level of contractors' activities are defined and redefined repeatedly, as demanded by budgetary cycles and the special events which intrude on these cycles from Washington and the field. But there are limitations on the ability of a small technical staff in Germantown to initiate, monitor, and, if necessary, redirect work at strong, remote technical establishments.

The weapons laboratories may serve as a case in point. It is not always easy to trace the source of new weapons ideas; some have stemmed from military requests and more, in all probability, from laboratory scientists. Indeed, men at the laboratories tend to be so far ahead of those in Washington in their grasp of technical possibilities that there can be a visible lag in comprehending what they are actually working on. "You try to keep them [the DOD and AEC] abreast of what you're doing," one scientist remarked, "and [yet] most of the time they don't realize what you're doing for six or nine months." Laboratory representatives meet frequently with staff of the AEC Division of Military Application and the Department of Defense (military officers are stationed permanently at Livermore and Albuquerque) to review the status of weapons programs; in addition, they serve often as advisers to DOD and the Commission in the formulation of weapons policies and requirements. The top secret documents that emerge from the AEC and/or DOD set forth long range objectives for nuclear weapons development, the status of current weapons development programs, 5-10 year projections of the laboratories' work and capabilities, nuclear testing plans (including contingency plans for resuming tests in environments now prohibited by treaty), and ten year stockpile projections.

Nonetheless, within this armamentarium of policy set at the highest levels of government, great authority has been delegated to the laboratory directors. They may initiate conceptual and feasibility studies without prior approval (required for developmental engineering and subsequent stages of weapons production)

[26] From "Request for Expression of Interest—Operation of Chemical Processing Facilities," AEC Richland Operations Office, April 3, 1964.

and, at least in recent years, no attempt has been made to "second guess" them[27] by obtaining independent evaluation of the technical quality of their work. The laboratories have been judged primarily by their results—weapon designs and (tested or expected) performance—and these have usually satisfied the AEC, the Armed Forces, and the Congress.

The difficulty of knowing what is really going on in a great laboratory and, in consequence, of giving realistic current commands even of a kind which the laboratory would welcome may be illustrated by an interesting, if awkward, episode. As former Commissioner Loren Olson has related it, the AEC instructed the weapons laboratories to prepare for a resumption of nuclear tests in 1961, but neither did so:

> . . . the AEC, of which I was a member at that time, directed the laboratory [Livermore; but the story was evidently similar at Los Alamos] to be ready for testing at least six months before the Russians resumed testing [September 1961], and we dug holes and reviewed shots and so forth for six months before the Russians started to test, and when the Russians *did* test, we asked for the program to go ahead with it, and then the director of the laboratory [John Foster] said, "Well, we can get started with some shots, but meaningful shots will be six or nine months off." We said, "Why, don't you have a program?" He said, "Well, my people didn't believe there was any chance of testing and you can't make these people work unless they believe in it."[28]

Foster has commented further that

> . . . an *administrative directive* (not a technical directive) was given to the Laboratory which instructed us to be ready to shoot, given a specific go-ahead from the AEC. No directive was given concerning the make up of the experiments, although the general planning was within the scope of the AEC approved program. Essentially the Laboratory had a free hand in the choice of shots. The fact of the matter is that the Laboratory did shoot as directed. It complied with the administra-

[27] The same point was made independently and the same phrase was used to make it by a member of the AEC Division of Military Applications and of the Livermore Laboratory.

[28] Remarks at the 1963 Annual Convention of the Federal Bar Association, Sheraton Hotel, Philadelphia (Sept. 25, 1963). See also John Finney's account of this episode, " '61 A.E.C. Order to Plan Tests Ignored," *New York Times* (Sept. 26, 1963), p. 11.

tive directive. Meaningful shots (i.e., shots meaningful from a long range experimental view) were not fired immediately as Mr. Olson indicated, and my reply to his question of "Why?" was essentially as . . . shown. . . . No scientist can plan an experiment in a field of advancing technology, to be executed on some future date, and then when that date comes and goes and the experiment is not accomplished, redesign the experiment for execution at a new future date and when that date comes and goes, continue the process again, and again, and again, and have that experiment be meaningful.[29]

Olson recounted this episode as a reply to charges by Lawrence Caruso (cited earlier) of excessive control by the AEC of its university research programs. However, the conclusion that reconciles the testimony of all three men (Olson, Foster, and Caruso), as well as of many others interviewed in the course of the present study, is that while the AEC has increased its administrative and cost controls and sheer paperwork in recent years to a point that many contractors consider excessive, it has generally not held a tight rein over the technical aspects of R&D programs. The principal exceptions have been the naval reactors and space propulsion programs, but the fact that these have been exceptions is suggested by the frequency with which the Joint Committee has pointed to them as models other AEC programs should emulate.

Additional examples of contractors' lag in implementing instructions (aggravated by the government's repeated failure to issue firm instructions) can be found in the motley record of the aircraft nuclear propulsion program. For instance, following a meeting with President Eisenhower in December 1956, it was decided to cancel the weapons system phase of the work. General Electric, the principal contractor for that system, was informed of this decision in January 1957 and, in a joint Air Force-AEC letter of February 13, 1957, was requested to submit by March 12 a revised program and budget for the year ending September 30, 1957, along indicated lines. However, agreement on the reoriented program was not reached until May 1957, because, as AEC General Manager Luedecke later told the Comptroller General, "the contractor was insisting upon a broader program than the Government considered necessary or desirable and . . . an earlier formali-

[29] Letter from John Foster, Aug. 18, 1965.

zation of the agreement could have been achieved only by acquiescing to the contractor's wishes. . ." (an argument to which the
Comptroller General took exception).[30] An even clearer instance
of General Electric's sluggish response to instruction has also been
documented by the Comptroller General:

GE did not take timely action to suspend certain work relating to
the nuclear operation of an unclad ceramic reactor. The Aircraft Nuclear Propulsion Office (ANPO) advised GE in July 1958 to cancel the
work, but it was not until after ANPO expressed deep concern in November 1958 over the amount of effort spent on ceramics that GE terminated the work in December 1958.[31]

Several additional observations appear warranted on this matter
of technical control.

1. Some contractors (and men) are obedient: others are not.
Some do what they are asked promptly, while others do what they
think they should—and the obedient contractors are by no means
invariably the best. Indeed, one contractor is privately disparaged
by many in the nuclear industry who consider the firm's excessive
obedience as an abject deferral to government contract officers of
business judgment and integrity. As Daniel Lang noted, following
his discussions with Los Alamos scientists in March 1958,
"Different men . . . react differently to Washington directives.
Some are quite literal about carrying them out. Middle-of-the-
roaders try to strike a balance between pleasing Washington and
following their own line of thought and research. Then, there are
those who consider themselves authoritatively in touch with the
situation at hand and who instinctively look upon the directives as
just a bureaucratic shuffling of papers."[32] Some strong and experienced operating contractors, who have prided themselves on their
initiative, suggest that all will *not* be well if the new breed of con-

[30] The Comptroller General commented that ". . . we do not believe that an early
settlement could have been achieved only by acquiescing to the contractor's wishes,
since the Government should be in a better position when negotiating for future
work than in negotiating for work already completed." *Review of Manned Aircraft Nuclear Propulsion Program, Atomic Energy Commission and Department of
Defense,* Comptroller General of the United States (February 1963), p. 56.

[31] *Ibid.,* p. 101.

[32] Daniel Lang, *From Hiroshima to the Moon* (Simon and Schuster, New York,
1959), p. 357.

tractor operating AEC facilities merely does what he is told. "The measure of [a contractor's] performance may then be on how well the detailed procedures and regulations have been followed rather than on how well the job has been accomplished."[33]

2. The shifting character and indecisiveness in the management of reactor development programs seemed particularly apparent during our 1964 visits to contractor establishments and AEC field offices. While basic research prospers on little direction, and the goals of bomb development are so clear that progress has not been slowed by the delegation of responsibility to the strong and capable weapons laboratories, the inadequate technical direction of civilian reactor programs was widely recognized. "There is no one at Germantown, even among the technical people, who worries solely about technical problems," an industry executive observed. "They are constantly diverted by the need to justify the program, and by other administrative and policy problems." Interviews conveyed the impression that the civilian reactor programs lacked a clear and coherent objective and effective management. When a contractor complained about the inability to get a prompt decision out of the AEC, it was almost invariably the Division of Reactor Development that he was talking about.

In part, the Division's problems reflected political-economic conflicts (between fossil and nuclear fuel interests, high and low fuel cost areas, firms with established and radically new reactor types, the "big two" [G.E. and Westinghouse] and "third echelon" companies, private and public laboratories—all within a budget that has been stabilized at $500 million or less during fiscal years 1964-66) in which the program has been entangled. The manifold purposes the program has striven to serve, the political crossfires in which it has been caught, and the periodic reversal or modification of staff technical judgments to comport with broader policy objectives have not facilitated decisive management. But, in part, the Division's problems were also managerial, a point which was recognized by the Commission when it initiated a substantial restaffing and reorganization of the Division in December 1964. Some critics thereupon complained that, where reactor development had previously been under-managed, it was now becoming

[33] Letter from a senior employee of a major AEC contractor, Aug. 13, 1965.

over-managed. It would be remarkable if a needed cure grew so quickly worse than the disease; we have no evidence to offer on the patient's present condition.

3. Managerial problems have also been encountered by interagency programs, in which the normal difficulties of making clear and firm technical decisions and conveying them to the contractor are compounded by the division of program responsibility among two or more agencies. The solution which the Joint Committee on Atomic Energy (JCAE) has espoused is patterned on that of Admiral Rickover's naval reactors group. Its principal ingredients are: the formulation of a clear objective; the establishment of a joint interagency office to implement it, to which is assigned responsibility for the entire project, including budgetary as well as technical aspects, and non-nuclear as well as nuclear components; the appointment of a forceful director authorized to make the necessary decisions and who therefore has a sufficient stake in the success of the program to stay on the job until it is finished. The main drawback of the system is the impracticability and undesirability of establishing a separate office—which is in many respects virtually an independent agency dealing directly with the Congress—for every program; and the fragmentation of agency programs, policies, and authority that results from doing so.

PART II

Dramatis Personae

CHAPTER VII

The Commission

In the course of the first public statement on August 6, 1945 announcing the development of an atomic bomb and its destruction of Hiroshima, President Truman said "I shall recommend that the Congress . . . consider promptly the establishment of an appropriate commission to control the production and use of atomic power with the United States."[1] During the debates that ensued over alternative legislative proposals, the choice of a commission or board to guide the new atomic agency was not at issue, although views differed on its appropriate size, whether military representatives should be included, the qualifications of members, and if they should serve full time (as was finally decided) or part time (as the May-Johnson bill had proposed). Responsibility for the direction of the strange and terrible enterprise should not, it was widely felt, be left to any one man. The exceptional secrecy with which nuclear affairs were conducted also called for special provisions to ensure that adequate weight would be given to the full range of national interests at stake, so that, for example, emphasis on the development of nuclear bombs would not lead to the neglect of other military and civilian applications of nuclear energy or of pure research in nuclear physics.

In the years that have followed, secrecy has waned, nuclear technology has advanced on many fronts with a safety record excelling that of many conventional industries, and, like villagers living beside a dormant volcano, the nation has grown accustomed to the

[1] Harry S. Truman, *Memoirs* (Doubleday & Co., New York, 1955), Vol. I, p. 423.

mounting international hoards of nuclear bombs. Familiarity has bred a growing criticism of the commission form of organization; a mechanism once praised for promoting wise, balanced, and non-partisan policies is increasingly condemned for precisely the same reasons, only what was deemed wisdom and balance is termed caution and timidity, while nonpartisanship is regarded as an abdication of executive and presidential responsibilities. Though the commission form cannot reasonably be criticized for operating as designed, it might reasonably be changed if it no longer suits the agency's major functions (which, many assert, involve more administration and less momentous policy-making than heretofore).

Already in 1949, the first Commission chairman, David Lilienthal, recommended to President Truman (who agreed) that "the Commission should be abolished and an Administrator substituted with an Advisory Board."[2] A similar suggestion was advanced in 1955 by David Teeple, a former staff member of the Joint Committee on Atomic Energy, as a solution to varied AEC ailments.[3] And in May 1962, all five Commissioners recommended to Budget Director David Bell that their jobs be abolished and replaced by a single administrator in order to speed up the process of decision and to establish clearer lines of responsibility within the agency:

[2] On November 18, 1949, Lilienthal met with Truman to discuss his forthcoming departure from the Commission and the choice of a successor. His journal entry for the day reads, ". . . I showed him a long memo on a successor, including some names. It began: the Commission should be abolished and an Administrator substituted with an Advisory Board. He said, 'That makes sense. . . .'" The entry for December 3, referring apparently to a recent meeting of the Commission, states, "Tuesday I blew open my feeling that the 'role of the Commission' had proved so difficult to define because a full-time Comm. was a mistake, under present circumstances, that it ought to be abolished and an Administrator plus part-time Comm. substituted . . . [Commissioner Gordon] Dean was 'shocked' and the others felt, I think, that I was unrealistic. . . ." *The Journals of David E. Lilienthal*, Vol. II, *The Atomic Energy Years, 1945-1950* (Harper & Row, New York, 1964), pp. 598, 603. See also James Reston, "Lilienthal for Single Head to Replace Atomic Body," *New York Times* (Feb. 21, 1950), p. 8.

[3] Teeple's view, put forward in a pamphleteering volume, was that "IMMEDIATE STEPS BE TAKEN . . . TO ESTABLISH AN EXECUTIVE DEPARTMENT OF ATOMIC ENERGY . . . AND THEREBY TO DEFINE THE POLITICAL RESPONSIBILITY AND THE AUTHORITY WHICH ARE LACKING UNDER THE PRESENT ORGANIZATION" *Atomic Energy: A Constructive Proposal* (Duell, Sloan and Pearce, New York, 1955), pp. 5-6, his capitals.

In recent years . . . the commission has become increasingly preoccupied with the civilian development of atomic energy, particularly with nuclear power reactors.

It is in coping with these broadening activities and responsibilities that many officials feel the commission has begun to demonstrate the inherent weakness of "administration by committee."

By law, each of the commissioners has "equal responsibility and authority in all decisions" and all actions are determined by a majority vote.

Both within the commission staff and among officials of other agencies dealing with the commission, there have been constant complaints of delays and difficulties encountered in obtaining decisions from the commission.

Another major complaint has concerned the lack of clear responsibility for decisions and actions within the commission. As one commission staff member described the situation: "It's like trying to grapple with five greased pigs."[4]

The proposal was reportedly endorsed by President Kennedy, who discussed it with Representative Chet Holifield, the Joint Committee chairman. However, hearings on the matter that Holifield announced for 1963 were subsequently dropped, presumably because of the committee's fear that its influence over AEC policy would diminish while that of the President would be enhanced under such a reorganization. The commission organization has not only given the AEC a degree of independence from presidential authority more characteristic of regulatory bodies—the "headless fourth branch" of government[5]—than of other executive agencies, but has enabled the Joint Committee to play on policy differences among the Commissioners so as to obtain infor-

[4] John Finney, "Kennedy Favors A One-Man A.E.C." *New York Times* (May 17, 1962); see also John Finney, "A.E.C. Is Weighing Abolishing Itself," *New York Times* (Nov. 18, 1962). Cf. the remarks of Craig Hosmer, senior Republican congressman on the Joint Committee, about "the characteristics of commission-type management which inevitably results in indecision, buck passing and reluctance to assume responsibility for hard decisions." *Congressonal Record* (Sept. 15, 1965) daily edition, p. 23143.

[5] "Subject to all three branches in specific respects, the commissions nevertheless evade complete and continuing control by any one of them. That is why they have sometimes been called the 'headless fourth branch' of the government." Former AEC Commissioner Thomas E. Murray, *Nuclear Policy for War and Peace* (The World Publishing Co., Cleveland and New York, 1960), p. 193.

mation on Commission deliberations and strengthen the committee's influence on program and policy formation.[6]

Differences among the Commissioners should not be exaggerated; throughout the AEC's history, the Commissioners appear to have made great efforts to achieve a harmony of outlook. Thus, from its inception in 1946 through July 1949, Commissioners recorded a dissenting vote (that of Lewis Strauss) in only 12 of over 500 formal decisions; and, from 1953 to 1958, only 70 split votes compared to 1,531 unanimous decisions.[7] But votes have often not been taken where a cleavage would be recorded, and some cleavages have involved major policy issues in which the dissenting Commissioner, aided by the Joint Committee, ultimately prevailed over the majority of his colleagues.[8]

A famous example was the success of Lewis Strauss and the Joint Committee in persuading President Truman to reverse the

[6] Cf. the observation of Harold Green, the principal student of the Joint Committee, that "In part . . . the JCAE has been able to thrive and expand through skillful utilization and exploitation of differences of opinion among the five commissioners." Or, as the still better authority, Representative Chet Holifield, put it, ". . . the Joint Committee could not have worked as efficiently had we not had the conflicts of ideas in this new field of endeavor presented to us. We could, in essence, look behind the recommendation of a single administrator and know what had occurred as a result of his recommendation by knowing the conflict of opinion or the difference in judgment of the Commissioners on a specified program. Many times the Commissioners come before us, and will say, well, four of us, or three of us think so and so, and the other man, or the other two men think so and so.

"We get the value of the independent viewpoint of the minority Commission members; then, we can exercise, in my opinion, much better judgment as to authorizing and funding a project if we have the story complete rather than the predigested recommendation of one man." Harold Green, "Atomic Energy: Commission or Administrator?" *Bulletin of the Atomic Scientists* (December 1962), p. 36; and *Proceedings,* Atomic Industrial Forum (1964 Annual Conference), Vol. 1, p. 36.

[7] See July 13, 1949 letter from David Lilienthal to Senator McMahon in *Investigation into the United States Atomic Energy Project,* Hearings before the Joint Committee on Atomic Energy, 81 Cong. 1 sess (May 25, 1947), Pt. 23, p. 1070; and Lewis Strauss, *Men and Decisions* (Doubleday & Co., Garden City, N. Y., 1962), p. 338.

[8] "The history of the Commission is noted for the occasions when capable individual Commissioners such as Lewis Strauss, Tom Murray, and Dr. Robert Wilson, starting from a minority position, subsequently succeeded in having their view become the majority position either of the Commission or impressed upon the Congress their minority position to where it was approved by our committee," Representative Chet Holifield in *Proceedings,* Atomic Industrial Forum (1964 Annual Conference), Vol. 1, p. 35.

Commission's decision not to push the development of a hydrogen bomb. A recent example appears to be Commissioner James Ramey's success in postponing efforts to reorganize the Commission. "By a 4 to 1 vote, the Commission reaffirmed its position that the time had come to replace the five-man Commission with a single administrator. The dissenter was James T. Ramey. . . ," John Finney has reported.[9] Lending support to the predilections of the Joint Committee, this vote of Ramey, former staff director of the committee, was evidently more successful in continuing the commission form than were the votes of the other four Commissioners in discontinuing it.

To be sure, the Joint Committee can exploit the views of a minority of the Commission only when a majority of the committee wishes to do so. Thus, during the Lilienthal Commission, the committee's Republican minority complained that "we requested and by committee vote were denied the opportunity to hold executive hearings to determine the nature of the dozen formal voting disagreements by Commissioner Strauss and the individual views thereon of the other Commissioners. . . ."[10] However, there have been relatively few episodes of this type, in which the committee has declined to obtain information from the Commission; they have usually involved information relevant to a partisan political issue.

From the earliest days to the present, critics have charged the Commission with timidity and indecision. Republican Senator Bourke Hickenlooper, who mounted a major attack on David Lilienthal and the Commission in 1949, declared that "The Atomic Energy Commission represents bureaucracy in its most perfect form." Although his accusations of "maladministration . . . equivocation, misplaced emphasis, and waste"[11] were rejected by the majority of the Joint Committee, they led to protracted hearings whose impact on the Commission was pronounced. "There arose a tendency . . . to approach projects and programs less from the

[9] *New York Times* (April 7, 1963).

[10] *Investigation into the United States Atomic Energy Commission,* Joint Committee on Atomic Energy, S. Rept. 1169, 81 Cong. 1 sess. (October 1949), p. 2.

[11] *Investigation into the United States Atomic Energy Project,* Hearings, *op. cit.,* Pt. 2, p. 25, and Pt. 23, p. 1113.

point of view 'Is this the best solution to the problem?' but 'Can we defend it?' The consequent defensive attitude . . . has continued even until today, and has produced a deterrent effect on arriving quickly at bold solutions to developmental and policy problems."[12]

The commission form of organization is, to be sure, designed for deliberateness rather than decisiveness. On top of that, the fact that commissioners serve full time and are held directly responsible by the Joint Committee for AEC programs has served to involve them in major contract awards, significant departures in programs and budgets, and, in general, in monitoring the status of AEC activities more closely than would a part time Commission. The contrast between the level of detail presented in congressional testimony by Commissioners and, for example, members of the part time National Science Board is marked. This tendency of Commissioners to get involved in day-to-day operations has been accentuated by their inclination to specialize in different AEC activities, and to defer to the specialties of their fellow Commissioners. The net effect, critics assert, is a dilution of individual responsibility, for each "specialist" Commissioner is sheltered and cannot be called to account for policies that are not his alone but those of the group. It is often said, also, that the Commissioners have given inadequate attention to the most important issues of national nuclear policy, many of which have, in consequence, been dealt with by the White House, the National Security Council, and high level interagency bodies. However, as the President, the Secretary of Defense and the Secretary of State, for example, would inevitably be closely involved in setting such critical policies as the use or disuse of nuclear weapons, it is difficult to assess the extent to which the AEC's role in these matters has or has not been impaired by its commission structure.

The Lilienthal Commission attempted to form its own judgment of the terms of several major contracts in abeyance when it took over from the Army (negotiations having been started by General Groves, but the final contracts having not yet been

[12] Arnold Kramish and Eugene Zuckert, *Atomic Energy for Your Business* (David McKay Co., New York, 1956), p. 114.

signed). However, the basic structure of contracting with a few firms and universities for the management of the nuclear production works and laboratories was retained. The Commission had enough problems of its own—learning just what the Army had bequeathed, setting up an accounting system, maintaining production in deteriorating plants, maintaining morale in laboratories from which there had been a mass exodus, worrying about security and political attacks—not to wish to upset the established system of contractors. Indeed, with technical knowledge closely guarded, fees low or absent, no private patent rights, and future civilian applications uncertain, there was no long queue of qualified companies applying for nuclear work; in the Manhattan Project and the early years of the Commission, a number of the major contractors, like Du Pont, General Electric, and Western Electric, had had to be induced to take on their responsibilities, at times by the personal appeal of the President. The demands of technical reliability and security also operated to perpetuate the restricted circle of operating contractors that the first Commission accepted and succeeding Commissions did not much disturb.

Now that the circle has been broken at Hanford, the Commissioners have again been actively involved in selecting operating contractors and examining important contract selections of regional AEC offices to determine if any should be changed for one or another policy reason, such as promoting a broader range of industrial participation.

The Commissioners, and especially their chairman (their principal public spokesman and representative in dealings with the President and the heads of other agencies), have inevitably been embroiled in political controversies over the government's nuclear policies. A long list of such controversies could be compiled, from the earlier years to today, manifested in such episodes as the Hickenlooper and Oppenheimer hearings; and the debates over the hydrogen bomb development, the Dixon-Yates contract, licenses to construct power reactors near metropolitan areas, the export of nuclear information, materials, reactors, and arms, and attempts to limit or ban nuclear tests. The AEC has been involved in its fair share of controversy. Nevertheless, the intensity of at least certain controversies has probably been tempered by the fact that, at any given time, some Commissioners have usually been chosen by different Presidents and have represented more than one party or sectional interest. Particularly in the area of contract awards, it can be argued that a commission of five men affords greater insulation from political pressures and personal preferences than a single agency head serving as a normal member of a President's administration. To the extent that this is true, a reorganization that replaced the Commissioners with a single administrator might improve the efficiency of administration while involving the agency more fully in the normal turmoil of domestic politics.

Contrariwise, it can be argued that to take the AEC out of politics is to take it out of this world. The only realistic choice is between a greater involvement in the politics of the Congress (i.e., the Joint Committee), as at present, or in the politics of the Presidency, whose hand would be strengthened by the installation of a single administrator.

The charges of excessive caution and indecision noted above should, however, be put in some perspective. It is strange that an agency against which such charges have so often (and, apparently, so justifiably!) been leveled should nonetheless have an outstanding record of technical achievement. The Commission has successfully produced a great quantity and variety of nuclear materials and weapons, has successfully developed nuclear reactors for naval propulsion, a nuclear ramjet engine, nuclear systems for auxiliary power, and is now (November 1966) past the threshold of developing nuclear reactors for the economic generation of electric power. Its most notable failures have been the billion dollar joint AEC-Air Force effort to develop a nuclear powered plane and a number of ill-starred reactor projects. The fate of other ventures, such as the nuclear powered rocket, breeder reactors, the use of nuclear explosives for excavations, or the release of energy from controlled hydrogen fusion, cannot yet be determined. On balance, the Commission may be judged an effective organization for the development of new nuclear, and particularly military, technology. It cannot yet be said to have been as effective in the development of *economic* technology; and, assuredly, it has been least successful at solving the dilemmas of the nuclear arms race, but this has neither been its primary responsibility nor has any other agency been notably more successful at that intractable task.[13]

[13] A long list of efforts to halt or control the arms race can, of course, be cited, from the Baruch Plan and the Atoms for Peace program, the International Conferences on the Peaceful Uses of Atomic Energy, and the founding of the International Atomic Energy Agency through the moratorium on nuclear bomb tests, the treaty banning atmospheric tests, and contemplated treaties to end underground tests, to hamper the acquisition of nuclear weapons by non-nuclear powers, to reduce existing weapons stockpiles, to halt increases in vehicles for delivering nuclear bombs, and to stop the production of fissionable material for weapons. The AEC has initiated some of these efforts and been actively involved in most, as expert consultants if not protagonists.

CHAPTER VIII

The Joint Committee
on Atomic Energy

As, in view of the special importance and secrecy of the nuclear enterprise, the 1946 Atomic Energy Act placed its administration in the hands of a Commission with unusual powers, so the act established a unique body to discharge the responsibilities of the Congress with regard to the new agency. The Joint Committee on Atomic Energy, which held its organizational meeting on August 2, 1946, the day after President Truman signed the act, "is the only such permanent joint committee with continuing legislative responsibility ever created."[1] Composed of nine members from each House, who have from the outset included congressmen of stature, seniority, and ability, the committee has exercised exceptional powers over the programs, policies, budgets, and even, at times, contractual choices and procedures of the Commission. Indeed, two students of the committee have termed it "in its sustained influence within the Congress, its impact and influence on the executive, and its accomplishments, probably the most powerful congressional committee in the history of the nation."[2] The committee's powers have derived from special statutory provisions,

[1] *Science and Technology Act of 1958,* Analysis and Summary Prepared by the Staff and submitted to the Senate Government Operations Committee, 85 Cong. 2 sess. (1958), S. Doc. 90, p. 38.

[2] Harold Green and Alan Rosenthal, *Government of the Atom* (Atherton Press, New York, 1963), p. 266.

154

the nature of the Commission, and the tenure, talent, and outlook of committee members and staff.

Section 15(b) of the 1946 statute declared that "The Commission shall keep the joint committee fully and currently informed with respect to the Commission's activities,"[3] ensuring that the committee received sufficient information about both classified and unclassified nuclear programs to sanction their objectives and monitor their progress on behalf of the Congress. Initially, the committee declined to receive top secret information about the size of the nation's nuclear arsenal, but that sort of self denial has been rare, and the committee is, these days, thoroughly briefed, in executive sessions, on nuclear stockpiles and production plans. While the committee has not insisted on seeing internal AEC staff papers and Commission minutes, it has undoubtedly seen many staff papers[4] and has obtained from Commissioners assurances that they would disclose their votes at Commission meetings:

In 1957, during confirmation hearings on the nomination of John S.

[3] Sec. 202 of the 1954 Atomic Energy Act added "with respect to *all* the Commission's activities" (our italics) and further required that "The Department of Defense shall keep the Joint Committee fully and currently informed with respect to all matters within the Department of Defense relating to the development, utilization, or application of atomic energy. Any Government Agency shall furnish any information requested by the Joint Committee with respect to the activities or responsibilities of that agency in the field of atomic energy."

[4] Joint Committee member Senator Henry Jackson has asked rhetorically, "Should the Committee insist upon seeing the internal staff papers of the Commission and the minutes of the Commission's meetings? The Committee has never so insisted, because the members respect the Commission's need for a certain privacy in its internal functioning." To John Palfrey (then a professor of law at Columbia and subsequently an AEC commissioner), however, it seemed clear that the Joint Committee had "access to internal documents of the Executive Branch of the Government of a kind available to no other Congressional committee." Green and Rosenthal have summed up the situation thus: "The Committee clearly believes that there is no information of any kind which the Commission has the right to withhold," though it may, at times, elect not to request certain information. "It is clear . . . that the JCAE does not recognize the validity of any claim of executive privilege with respect to atomic-energy information possessed by the AEC and the Department of Defense." See Henry M. Jackson, "Congress and the Atom," *Annals of the American Academy of Political and Social Science* (November 1953), p. 77; John Palfrey, "Atomic Energy Law in the United States" in Herbert Marks, ed., *Law and Administration*, Series X, Progress in Nuclear Energy, Vol. 1. (Pergamon Press, London, 1959), p. 19; and Harold Green and Alan Rosenthal, *Government of the Atom*, pp. 102-03 and additional references cited there.

Graham, the Committee elicited his commitment that he would inform the JCAE [Joint Committee on Atomic Energy] of his own votes as a commissioner and that he would personally bring to the attention of the Committee any matter on which he felt that the JCAE should be informed if it were not otherwise informed. The latter pledge was also made by Commissioner John F. Floberg. . . . The present chairman, Dr. Glenn T. Seaborg, pledged that he would keep the JCAE informed on pending matters, rather than after action had taken place. . . . Similar commitments were extracted from Commissioner Leland J. Haworth.[5]

The Joint Committee has been the only committee of the Congress to have available for inspection the personnel security files, including the FBI investigative reports, of agency eemployees.[6] It is normally not merely informed about but familiar with significant issues confronting the Commission well before the Commission acts upon them.

As the Commission has usually found the Joint Committee its staunchest ally and protagonist in its efforts to win approval for new or expanded nuclear programs from the White House or other executive agencies, AEC Commissioners and staff have generally kept the committee well informed about their activities, plans, and problems. When this has not been done to the committee's satisfaction, as during periods of Lewis Strauss' chairmanship from 1953-58,[7] the committee has fought hard, resourcefully, and,

[5] Harold Green and Alan Rosenthal, op. cit., pp. 100-01.

[6] ". . . the Commission has always made available to the joint committee upon request the personnel security files of all persons employed in the [atomic energy] program for study and scrutiny by the members and by designated members of the staff of the joint committee. . . . This close relationship has not been, in any way, disturbed by the President's directive of March 13, 1948, prohibiting the delivery of personnel security files to congressional committees by executive agencies without prior approval of the President. . . . the Atomic Energy Commission at the time this directive was issued worked out special procedures with the Attorney General whereby the joint committee, provided strict confidence is maintained, continued to receive, upon request, the personnel security files. . . ." From June 6, 1949 letter of Chairman Lilienthal to Senator McMahon in Investigation into the United States Atomic Energy Project, Hearings before the Joint Committee on Atomic Energy, 81 Cong. 1 sess. (1949), Pt. 4, p. 155.

[7] The emphasis here should be put on the committee's, or certain of its members', satisfaction. The contention that the AEC then failed to keep the committee adequately informed was repeated during the 1959 hearings on Admiral Strauss'

for the most part, successfully to maintain its prerogatives. "When Jim Ramey came in" [as Joint Committee staff director in 1955], Senator Clinton Anderson, Chairman Strauss' bitter antagonist, has remarked, "we told him to watch the AEC. If we found they'd swept out the office and hadn't told us about it, we had somebody down there to find out why."[8]

There is evidence that the degree of AEC participation in interagency deliberations on high national nuclear policies has been reduced, at times, in order to protect executive confidences from premature disclosure to the Joint Committee. For example, when on January 31, 1950, Commissioners Lilienthal and Smyth, Secretary of State Acheson, and Secretary of Defense Johnson, as members of the Special Committee of the National Security Council on the Super Bomb, were discussing the phrasing of a recommendation to be handed to President Truman later in the day, "That the President direct the Secretary of State and the Secretary of Defense to undertake a reexamination of our objectives in peace and war and of the effect of these objectives on our strategic plans, in the light of the probable fission bomb capability and possible thermonuclear bomb capability of the Soviet Union," the omission of the chairman of the Atomic Energy Commission was noted.

Secretary Acheson said there was the . . . difficulty that under the law and the Commission's practice the Joint Committee on Atomic Energy was kept informed by the Commission on almost a day-to-day basis; that the inclusion of the Commission in this study would doubtless require that the current investigation into this matter be supplied to the Joint Committee while the discussions were tentative and even though they included matters of the utmost secrecy; this was a major objection.

I [Lilienthal] said that I could not say this was not a valid point. Dr. Smyth said he was inclined to agree that this was a real point. . . .

confirmation as Secretary of Commerce. Strauss termed it politically motivated and unfounded in fact, citing corroborative evidence from two of the three Joint Committee chairmen during those years, Representatives Sterling Cole and Carl Durham, and noting that AEC communications to the committee had more than doubled during his chairmanship. See Lewis L. Strauss, *Men and Decisions* (Doubleday & Co., New York, 1962), pp. 382-83.

[8] "Thinking Ahead with . . . Clinton P. Anderson" (interview with Senator Anderson), *International Science and Technology* (April 1964), p. 62.

Admiral Souers [Executive Secretary of the National Security Council] concurred. . . .[9]

In a significant 1963 address, Commissioner John Palfrey pointed out that "To an increasing extent, the atomic energy enterprise has spread throughout the government and has had to be conducted by the AEC in conjunction with other agencies. . . . [it] is coordinated at the White House level, by the President himself, by his staff members concerned with national security, and by his assistants on matters of science and technology and, as usual, or more than usual, by the Bureau of the Budget." He asked the Joint Committee to exercise restraint in its requests for information on interagency and White House consultations, so as to preserve the influence of the committee and the Commission on nuclear policies of the greatest national importance:

. . . the Commission's practice over the years has been to inform the Committee of developments before the Commission has reached a decision. When these developments involve a number of other agencies which do not ordinarily maintain such a close working relationship with Congressional committees, a sensible accommodation will have to be sought. . . .

. . . the Commission cannot be an automatic pipeline to Congress on everything it learns from another agency relating to the atom. . . . By pushing somewhat less hard, in interagency matters, the Committee enables the Commission to remain at the center of the atomic picture. . . .[10]

The Joint Committee need not, of course, rely for its information only on the Commissioners and AEC headquarters staff. The committee is a center of efforts by proponents of public or private power, by mining, industrial, and labor groups seeking to promote

[9] *The Journals of David E. Lilienthal, op. cit.,* Vol. II, pp. 624, 631.

[10] John Palfrey, "The End of the Sacred Atomic Preserve," remarks before the American Nuclear Society (Chicago, Dec. 5, 1963). Not three months later, Joint Committee members Senator Pastore and Representative Hosmer, through astute and persistent questioning, gleaned from a reluctant Palfrey the composition of an interagency committee considering government policy on the use of nuclear explosives in cratering experiments. See *AEC Authorizing Legislation Fiscal Year 1965,* Hearings before the Joint Committee on Atomic Energy, 88 Cong. 2 sess. (1964), Pt. 3, pp. 1229-31.

or defend their stake in nuclear developments. University scientists and administrators, laboratory directors, executives of companies with large AEC contracts, the stronger directors of AEC regional offices, and influential local citizens may volunteer information, or provide it privately upon request, particularly to committee members from their own state. Thus, Senator Henry Jackson has been an important figure in the affairs of Hanford; Senator Clinton Anderson, in developments at Los Alamos and Sandia; Senator Albert Gore has maintained a special interest in Oak Ridge, Representatives Chet Holifield and Craig Hosmer in the Lawrence Radiation Laboratory and the Stanford linear accelerator, Representative Melvin Price in Argonne, and so on. In addition, the committee has usually been well served by an able, aggressive, bipartisan staff (comprising some seven professional and sixteen clerical and secretarial personnel, as of March 1964), chosen jointly by the two ranking Democratic and Republican members,[11] and has, from time to time, retained as consultants authorities on nuclear science and technology and at least three former Commissioners, Lewis Strauss, Gordon Dean, and Thomas Murray.

But final credit for their knowledge of nuclear affairs must be assigned to committee members themselves, the senior of whom have over the years acquired broad experience and an insight into policy issues often surpassing that of the more transient Commissioners. Four members, Senators Richard Russell and Bourke Hickenlooper and Representatives Chet Holifield and Melvin

[11] Green and Rosenthal, *op. cit.*, p. 66. At the outset, the professional staff consisted of two former Manhattan District security officers, David Teeple and Fred Rhodes, "both doubtless competent men in their field, but . . . with no claim to special competence outside their one field." Former Commissioner W. W. Waymack, "Four Years Under Law," *Bulletin of the Atomic Scientists* (February 1951), p. 54. The AEC suggested that the committee hire a few scientists, but, according to one informant, the committee's Republican majority felt that "atomic scientists, particularly theoretical physicists, were Democratic in their political sympathies." This political explanation was disputed by another informant who suggested that scientists were not employed simply because it was feared that they might not preserve the necessary degree of confidence about committee affairs in the course of their relations with professional colleagues and the public. (See also footnote 15, Chapter X.)

Price, have been on the committee continuously from 1946 to date (Dec. 1966); each year from 1955-60, the average duration of committee members' service ranged from 5.5 to 7.0 years. By contrast, as of May 1965, the AEC had had 26 Commissioners who had served, on average, a little more than three years.[12] Stability of membership has been enhanced by the statutory provision that not more than five of the nine members from each House shall come from the majority party. In its periodic contests with the Commission, Craig Hosmer has observed, "the Joint Committee has had such a permanency in its membership, whereas the Commission has had such a turnover in membership, the Joint Committee has had a degree of advantage . . . that has in many instances left it the winner. . . ."[13]

At the outset, members of the Joint Committee seemed either overawed by, or uninformed about, the atom and made few efforts to influence nuclear policies, confining themselves largely to inquiries about the efficiency of AEC administration and, especially, security procedures. Noting that the JCAE "appears to have gone to considerable pains to avoid any active participation in the policy area," one scholar even complained that it had failed to "accept any broad responsibility" for AEC programs.[14]

This novel phase ended with the 1949-50 battle over the hydrogen bomb development, in which the Joint Committee, siding with the Department of Defense and dissident AEC Commissioners and scientists, persuaded President Truman to overrule Chairman Lilienthal and the AEC General Advisory Committee. The vast expansion of plant for the production of nuclear materials, in the years immediately following, to implement Truman's decision and to outproduce the Russians, has been the single most important achievement that can be credited to the JCAE. For it led before long to the era of nuclear plenty with the diversification of nuclear

[12] Green and Rosenthal, op. cit., p. 33; and Melvin Price, remarks on "The Congress" at the Brookings Institution, Jan. 26, 1965.

[13] Craig Hosmer, "Policy Objectives and Government Organization—A Panel Discussion," Atom Forum 1962, Proceedings of the Annual Conference, November 26, 27, 28, 1962 (Atomic Industrial Forum, New York, 1963), p. 70.

[14] Morgan Thomas, Atomic Energy and Congress (University of Michigan, Ann Arbor, 1956), pp. 31, 69.

weapons and strategies, the promotion of other major military and civilian uses for nuclear materials, and all the problems of subsidies, embarrassingly large hoards, and eventual economic dislocation characteristic of other too-successful government critical commodity stockpiling programs. It also set the seal on the Joint Committee's philosophy, which has been expansionist and aggressive in comparison to the relative caution of the Commission. ". . . if the Committee has a single general comment to offer," the Joint Committee declared in 1951, "it is this: Greater boldness and more scientific and technical daring should be brought to bear upon the program."[15] The committee has consistently urged "a vigorous, imaginative, and aggressive atomic-energy program, demanding boldness and risk-taking rather than caution and economy."[16]

Although its success has varied with political circumstances and the extent to which the Commission chairman and the President have contested its role, the Joint Committee has since striven to act like a congressional board of directors for the government's nuclear enterprise.[17] ". . . it can be said," Senator Jackson asserted as far back as 1953, "that the Committee made the decisions, with the advice and consent of the executive branch."[18] Among the significant programs for which the committee has taken credit, in addition to the hydrogen bomb and plant expansion, there may be listed: the development of nuclear powered submarines and other naval and maritime ships, the effort to develop a nuclear powered airplane, expanded programs to develop nuclear electric power

[15] Joint Committee on Atomic Energy, S. Rept. 1041, 82 Cong. 1 sess. (1951), p. 7.

[16] Green and Rosenthal, *op. cit.*, p. 105.

[17] This "board of directors" characterization was suggested by an industry spokesman in a 1963 interview; he pointed out that the Commissioners have often taken a more detached view of the AEC, being inclined even to cut back or dispose of certain programs and facilities, against the wishes of the committee and of AEC and contractor staff. The same phrase was used by Representative Melvin Price in a 1956 address; he described the committee as "a sort of over-all board of directors for the atomic-energy enterprise in coming up with recommendations and suggestions as to courses of action. . . ." (cited in Green and Rosenthal, *op. cit.*, p. 109. footnote).

[18] See Henry M. Jackson, "Congress and the Atom," *Annals of the American Academy of Political and Social Science* (November 1953), p. 76.

stations, the development of light atomic bombs that can be carried by fighter planes,[19] and the installation of electronic controls on nuclear weapons.[20]

To be sure, cynical observers have noted, the Joint Committee has been more prone to claim responsibility for the successes than for the failures of nuclear programs; credit can be assumed more readily than it can be assigned—"Whatever the Joint Committee may be," one informant remarked, "it is not modest"; and, during some of the happiest periods of Commission-committee relations, the Commission has exercised restraint in blowing its own trumpet.

"What about the award of contracts? What about the hiring of personnel—and the selection of plant sites? Should we on the Committee intervene in these matters? In fact we do not intervene. We have followed a strictly hands-off policy—and rightly so."[21] Granted, Senator Jackson made these remarks in 1952 and might either modify them today or put a technical construction on "intervene." No Joint Committee representative sits on an AEC

[19] ". . . a few years ago, many military experts insisted that atomic bombs could never be carried by fighter planes against tactical targets; they argued that the bomb simply could not be made small enough or light enough. . . . Many of the Committee members . . . urged—years before the doctrine gained wide acceptance in the Pentagon—that atomic weapons could and should be adapted to tactical uses" (ibid., p. 78).

[20] "Back in 1958 and 1959 the Joint Committee and its staff became uneasy about the safety and custody of nuclear weapons, particularly those assigned to NATO. . . . In the summer of 1960, as Chairman of the Joint Committee, I authorized a staff study of these problems. That fall and winter I approved an inspection trip by a special ad hoc subcommittee under the chairmanship of Representative Chet Holifield. The members visited 8 European countries and more than 15 nuclear weapon installations in November and December of 1960. . . .

"On February 15, 1961 . . . the top secret ad hoc report was sent to the President by Chairman Holifield. . . . the idea of utilizing various electromechanical devices to improve U. S. custody and control of nuclear weapons originated with . . . our staff director [James Ramey]. . . . Fortunately the White House, the Atomic Energy Commission and the Department of Defense have taken our ad hoc committee's report very seriously. . . . We are gratified that the executive branch is going forward with the development of these devices." Senator Clinton Anderson in Congressional Record (July 10, 1962), pp. 13056-57.

[21] Henry M. Jackson, "The Joint Committee—Something New in Government," Atomic Energy Industrial and Legal Problems (University of Michigan Law School, Ann Arbor, 1952), p. 244.

contract selection board or attends Commission meetings at which the recommendations of the board and of the cognizant AEC field office manager are reviewed. But the Senator was too modest in assessing the JCAE's influence on contract policy, contract terms, and particular contract awards, as attested both by the formal record and by informal testimony of qualified observers.

This is not to suggest that congressmen have employed improper means to obtain AEC contracts for firms in which they or their constituents have had a financial interest. (Although it has been asserted that Senator Robert Kerr of Oklahoma—never a member of the Joint Committee—did, in fact, benefit substantially from uranium procurement policies which he was influential in maintaining;[22] and a Commission chairman has recorded an episode of a kind that must have occurred more than once over the years in which a Joint Committee member complained that contractors in his state "were not getting a look-in" on AEC work.)[23] But the Joint Committee has played a significant role in the AEC system of contracting, one that has not been confined to influencing

[22] "Of the $2,274,000,000 worth of uranium that the Government will have purchased between 1959 and 1966, 16.5 percent, or about $375,000,000, will have come from mines owned or controlled by Kerr-McGee Oil Industries, Inc., of which Senator Kerr is board chairman." John Finney, "A.E.C. Will Buy More Uranium, Despite Surplus, to Aid Mining," *New York Times* (Nov. 20, 1962), p. 18. Cf. the *Washington Post's* call for ending "any unwarranted enrichment for favored individuals" by AEC uranium purchases: ". . . four corporations supply 50 percent of the Government's uranium, and the largest supplier is Kerr-McGee Oil Industries, Inc. . . . It is one thing for Congress to keep essential defense industries from folding up and quite another thing to pour enormous sums into the operations of big corporations owned by powerful members of Congress." Editorial (Nov. 29, 1962). Senator Kerr was never a member of the Joint Committee but congressmen from major uranium producing states such as Colorado, New Mexico, and Utah have been consistently represented.

[23] David Lilienthal's journal entry for Feb. 15, 1949 reads: "Last evening had a session with [Senator] Clint Anderson. Complaining about the fact that New Mexico contractors were not getting a look-in on work at Los Alamos. I managed to keep pleasant, keeping the discussion straight. Tyler [Navy Captain C. L. Tyler, the AEC representative in the area] answered most of the objections. I said there was only one subject that wasn't open for discussion: 'Tyler here is as honest as my father, and that is as straight as I can make it.'"

"When it was all over . . . Anderson said to me, 'I have to do this for those fellows. Tyler is a fine man and they all trust him out there.'" *The Journals of David E. Lilienthal, op. cit.,* Vol. II, p. 476.

nuclear policies and programs but has, at times, extended to the kind of review and recommendation on specific contracts that is normally a function of the executive branch.

Constituency interest cannot be said to have influenced the original location of most major AEC installations, which were determined primarily by technical requirements. However, the subsequent importance of these installations to the economy of their state and region has been reflected in the composition of the Joint Committee. Thus, of the four states with the largest AEC expenditures in fiscal year 1963, three (New Mexico, California, and Washington) had two representatives on the Joint Committee and the fourth (Tennessee), one, although the next four states (Ohio, Nevada, New York, and South Carolina) had none and the committee chairman, Senator Pastore, came from a state whose contractors received only $540,000 from the AEC. ". . . members indulge one another's regional or state interests in return for like indulgences . . . internal divisions of the Committee are seldom provoked by geographical factors."[24] The general consequences of constituency representation have probably been to strengthen the claims of established laboratories upon the AEC budget, reducing the Commission's flexibility in allocating R&D funds, and to set the production of uranium and nuclear materials at rates governed not only by demonstrable short-term military requirements but also by anticipated or hoped-for long term civilian demands and a wish to moderate the economic impact of rapid cuts upon the affected industries and localities.

An example of direct intervention by the Congress to change the terms of specific contracts occurred in the spring of 1950, when the Independent Offices subcommittee of the House put a rider on the AEC appropriations bill for fiscal year 1951 limiting the fee for the management of the towns of Oak Ridge and Los Alamos to $90,000.[25] The AEC had "argued that the contractors will not ac-

[24] Green and Rosenthal, *op. cit.*, pp. 45-46.

[25] The Roane-Anderson Company's annual fee for the management of Oak Ridge had previously been $180,000, and the Zia Company's fee for the management of Los Alamos, $154,000. Public Law 759—81st Congress stated that ". . . no part of the foregoing appropriation or contract authorization shall be used in connection with the payment of a fixed fee to any contractor or firm of contractors engaged under a cost-plus-a-fixed-fee contract or contracts at any installation of the Com-

cept less [than they had been receiving, and] . . . warned that the abrogation of existing, legally valid contracts will jeopardize the AEC's efforts to induce private firms to enter the atomic energy program."[26] One contractor (Roane-Anderson) terminated its contract as a result of the congressional action,[27] but the other (the Zia Company) accepted the reduced fee and the limitation was retained in subsequent appropriation acts.

The most celebrated display of the Joint Committee's prowess in the realm of contracting was afforded by a portion of the AEC Authorization Act for 1958, which reflected the dissatisfaction of the Democratic Congress with the nature and scale of the AEC civilian power reactor program, following the defeat of the 1956 Gore-Holifield bill that would have greatly expanded it. The Authorization Act required that before the AEC could complete any contractual arrangement for a civilian nuclear power reactor, "the general features of the proposed arrangement . . . shall be submitted to the Joint Committee, and a period of forty-five days shall elapse while the Congress is in session," prompting one commentator to declare that "The Joint Committee . . . has seized control over the civilian atomic power program and has stripped the AEC of a large measure of the responsibility, authority, and discretion which it previously had possessed and which executive agencies normally possess."[28]

The provision was patterned after section 164 of the 1954 Atomic Energy Act, which required that any new electric utility contract for the Oak Ridge, Paducah, and Portsmouth installations "shall be submitted to the Joint Committee and a period of thirty days shall elapse while Congress is in session . . . before the contract . . . shall become effective. . . ." In adopting this section, "Congress made clear that it did not intend to require Joint Committee 'approval' of such contracts, but merely to give Congress an

---

mission, where that fee for community management is at a rate in excess of $90,000 per annum. . . ."

[26] *Bulletin of the Atomic Scientists* (July 1950), p. 222.

[27] Roane-Anderson also filed suit in the U. S. Court of Claims to collect part of the reduced fee; the government agreed to a settlement of $58,986 (see *Court of Claims Reports*, 1954, Vol. 127, p. 827).

[28] Harold Green, "The Strange Case of Nuclear Power," *The Federal Bar Journal* (April-June 1957), p. 124.

opportunity by legislation to withdraw the authority to make such a contract. Congress clearly sought to avoid the constitutional problems which would be raised by a grant of authority to a congressional committee to validate or invalidate a contract. . . ."[29]

However, the majority report adopted by the Democratic members and Republican Senators of the Joint Committee, which accompanied the authorization bill, made crystal clear the committee's intent to instruct the Republican chairman of the Commission on how and with whom the Commission should execute a number of experimental reactor contracts. The following is only part of the extensive catalog of contractual advice volunteered by the committee:

 . . . the committee is of the opinion that the Commission should be required to change its methods of contracting for the reactor projects carried on with publicly owned and cooperative organizations in accordance with the principles discussed below. . . .

The following general principles as to changed contractual requirements are intended by the committee to be established:

1. AEC should contract directly with the equipment manufacturer for the development and construction of the reactor. Some protection of the equipment manufacturer for increases in cost arising out of developmental problems beyond its control should be provided on a cost-sharing basis.

2. AEC should also have a contract with the cooperative or publicly owned organization whereby the organization would lease the site to AEC, provide the conventional facilities, operate the entire plant, and buy steam from AEC. . . .

 . . . the committee has voted to make available to the AEC an additional sum of $1,500,000 for research and development in the art of the fast breeder reactor generally, anticipating that this special sum will be expended by AEC in its own laboratories. . . .

The committee is of the opinion that . . . the Commission should consider the development of a dual-purpose reactor for the following reasons: . . . The Commission, the General Electric Co., and AEC supporting laboratories have had a great deal of experience with the Hanford-type reactor, so progress should be relatively rapid. . . .

The committee is of the opinion that the smallest practicable prototype of a natural uranium gas-cooled reactor should be designed and

---

[29] James L. Morrisson, "Federal Support of Domestic Atomic Power Development—the Policy Issues," *Vanderbilt Law Review,* Vol. 12 (1959), p. 220.

constructed as soon as practicable. . . . In view of the availability of the AEC installation at Bettis and Idaho, including able designers and engineers of the [Westinghouse] Bettis group, and the willingness of Admiral Rickover to undertake direction of a gas-cooled reactor project, it would appear essential that this project be assigned to the Naval Reactors Branch under Admiral Rickover. . . .

. . . Since the plutonium recycle work has been carried on by the Hanford installation, it would appear appropriate that the experimental recycle reactor be constructed there.

The committee also heard testimony on the natural-uranium, heavy-water moderated and cooled reactor concept by the duPont Company representatives who have a modest development and feasibility study underway. It is believed that effort on this and similar projects should be increased by the Commission.

The majority report was necessary and justified, one informant stated, to protect public power interests against the financial hazards to which they would otherwise have been exposed by AEC policy.[30] They were, in short, part of the continuing controversy between the public and private power proponents that had flared up three years earlier over the Dixon-Yates contract.

In their minority report, the committee's House Republican members offered the following reflections on this virtuoso performance by the committee majority:

It is the stated intent of the majority that the gas-cooled reactor be built in order to permit Admiral Rickover and the Westinghouse Co. to have a project on which their staff can work. . . .

It is absolutely improper for this committee to shop around for a project to award to one industrial group merely to keep the group together. . . .

If, as, when, and where, the Commission decides that it should . . . construct another gas-cooled reactor, it should to the extent possible do

[30] ". . . the Commission had it set up to treat the [publicly owned power] cooperative like a private company, with the risk of loss being on the cooperative, which had no [financial] reserves; and since these [reactors] were experimental devices, to put the risk of loss on them could put them in bankruptcy—and———— [a senator on the Joint Committee] remarked that some people on the Commission might have wanted this. The law was changed so that the Commission would contract with the [reactor manufacturing] company, and take the risk, and the experience has shown this was right, since the [initial] cost estimates were lower than later developed. . . . It was a proper function of the [Joint] Committee to say [that] the Commission should contract directly and absorb the risk."

it on competitive bidding, if not on negotiation, after giving all others interested an opportunity to present their proposals. We believe Admiral Rickover would be the first to be embarrassed by this form of industrial favoritism. . . .

Rather than turning to the Congress, we think the Westinghouse people should redraft their own proposals and submit them to the Commission and to others interested in the industry. . . .

In the same way there have been many statements made by members of the majority that the natural uranium heavy water project is being proposed by them "in order to help Zinn." It was only last year that Dr. Zinn was a consultant to the Joint Committee. . . . We think he would be the first to object to a form of favoritism. . . . Here again, we believe that the project should be one for which the Commission after deciding it wants to go ahead, should seek proposals and, if desirable, competitive bids. . . .

By these amendments, the Joint Committee puts itself in the place of the Commission in the making of arrangements and letting of contracts and the pricing of proposals. In addition, it would replace the judgment of the Commission—the authority so designated by the Atomic Energy Act of 1954—with its own judgment as to the needs of the types of reactors to be built in the atomic energy program.[31]

Noting that "Congressional directions to the AEC to build reactors of specified types and characteristics . . . invite individuals . . . who have been unsuccessful in selling a proposal to the AEC, to have a second bite at the cherry before the [Joint Committee]" and that "congressional designation of particular contractors is a clear invasion of the executive function," a former member of the AEC's General Counsel's office expressed the hope that the 1958 authorization act and the committee majority report represented "the high water mark of legislative encroachment on the executive function."[32] However, the committee has shown little disposition to reduce its authority over the Commission merely because the committee majority, the Commission chairman, and the President have been adherents of the same political party. The AEC Authorization Acts for 1963 and 1964 again included provisions for a

[31] *Authorizing Appropriations for the Atomic Energy Commission,* Joint Committee on Atomic Energy, H. Rept. 978, 85 Cong. 1 sess. (1957); majority report extracts from pp. 17-20, 25, 26, 28; minority report, pp. 52-54.

[32] James Morrisson, *op. cit.,* pp. 220-21.

45-day period of review by the Joint Committee of certain Commission contracts,[33] and, in 1964, the committee acquired for the first time the power to authorize all of the Commission's operating expenditures. (This was an annual *cost*, rather than an *obligation*, authorization, enabling the committee to monitor more closely and more frequently what the AEC actually did.) The propensity of committee members to advise the Commission on whom it should contract with for various R&D projects continues unabated, as the following extracts from recent hearings demonstrate:

[Committee Chairman Chet Holifield, opposing a contract to private industry:] It seems to me it would be better to put this type of a preliminary experimental reactor, making it as wide as possible in its scope for the whole fast breeder art, into a national laboratory. . . . You have people there that are going to drift away if they are not given a function to perform. . . . GE has just about got the market pretty well covered at this time. . . . I think this is a project that ought to go to the national laboratory.[34]

[Representative Craig Hosmer, criticizing the award to General Motors of a contract for a military compact reactor (MCR):] I have nothing against GM. But GM has not put a cent of money in the nuclear business up until now when it looks like it is going to have a big MCR program. We have plenty of contractors that have gone into the hole who put a lot of money in this field. I do not know why the Commission at this time should be encouraging another one to get in when we have too many in already. . . . I have no brief for United Nuclear but I do have confidence in what they were doing in the nuclear field and I do not have confidence in what GM was doing.[35]

It is widely believed that the Joint Committee exercises a distinct influence on contract awards—not necessarily by "pulling strings," but simply by being there, for as the views and interests

[33] The AEC Authorization Act for Fiscal Year 1963 provided for a 45 day period of submission to the Joint Committee before the completion of any arrangement for the development, design, construction or operation of an organic power reactor or for the generation or sale of power from the Hanford New Production Reactor; and the Authorization Act for 1964 for the development, design, construction, and operation of a spectral shift nuclear power plant.

[34] *AEC Authorizing Legislation Fiscal Year 1963*, Hearings before the Joint Committee on Atomic Energy, 87 Cong. 2 sess. (1962), p. 466.

[35] *AEC Authorizing Legislation Fiscal Year 1965*, Hearings before the Joint Committee on Atomic Energy, 88 Cong. 2 sess. (1964), Pt. 2, p. 455.

TABLE 13

Attendance of Joint Committee Members at AEC Authorization Hearings, 1964 and 1965[a]

	Total	1964	1965
Days of hearings	34	18	16
House Members			
Man-days of attendance			
Possible	306	162	144
Actual	153	79	74
Average	4.5	4.4	4.6
Melvin Price (D., Ill.)	26	11	15
Chet Holifield (D., Calif.)	24	17	7
Craig Hosmer (R., Calif.)	24	10	14
Thomas Morris (D., N.M.)	20	6	14
John Anderson (R., Ill.)	20	12	8
William Bates (R., Mass.)	15	6	9
Jack Westland (R., Wash.)	12	12	b
Wayne Aspinall (D., Colo.)	9	6	3
William McCulloch (R., Ohio)	4	b	4
Albert Thomas (D., Texas)	0	0	0
Senate Members			
Man-days of attendance			
Possible	306	162	144
Actual	45	20	25
Average	1.3	1.1	1.6
John Pastore (D., R.I.)	15	11	4
George Aiken (R., Vt.)	9	3	6
Clinton Anderson (D., N.M.)	8	1	7
Albert Gore (D., Tenn.)	5	0	5
Henry Jackson (D., Wash.)	3	2	1
Wallace Bennett (R., Utah)	3	0	3
Bourke Hickenlooper (R., Iowa)	1	0	1
Carl Curtis (R., Neb.)	1	0	1
Richard Russell (D., Ga.)	0	0	0

[a] Attendance for at least part of each day's open or executive hearings on *AEC Authorizing Legislation for Fiscal Year 1965* (Jan. 27-March 3, 1964) or *Fiscal Year 1966* (Jan. 27-April 13, 1965) as recorded in the hearings of the Joint Committee on Atomic Energy.

[b] Not on the committee at the time.

of committee members are known to Commission staff, they constitute an important feature of the terrain the Commission must traverse in reaching major decisions. Indeed, the Commission's sensitivity to committee opinion may extend to details of contract administration. At any rate, in the course of a 1963 interview, one industry executive claimed that, during the last five to eight years, significant contract changes were increasingly checked out by the AEC with Joint Committee staff before they would be authorized by the contract officer.

This prevalent view is disputed by some whose intimate knowledge of the committee gives their judgment special weight. One such informant declared, "The Joint Committee has probably been *less* interested in contracts than most [congressional] committees," being more concerned with issues in the public arena of national nuclear policies. When representing the interests of constituents in particular contracts, he noted, members have rarely made use of committee staff but have acted, instead, in their capacity as individual congressmen. "It is remarkable how little intervention you get [from Joint Committee members] on contract matters."

In recent years, as the AEC budget has been stabilized or slightly reduced, and demands for the increased production of nuclear and thermonuclear weapons have been met, there has been an apparent slackening of interest in the affairs of the Joint Committee by some of its senior Senate members. "This is no longer a Joint Committee; it is a House Committee," one observer remarked, and an examination of attendance at hearings bears him out (Table 13). On the average, only one Senator (usually Pastore, Joint Committee chairman that year) attended each day's authorization hearings in 1964, and less than two, the following year. The Senators remain, of course, alert to and active in protecting the nuclear interests of their area; but they have been content to let the House members and committee staff assume much of the burden of hearings and monitoring Commission activities.

CHAPTER IX

The Department of Defense

The Department of Defense is, of course, the AEC's principal client, who must be satisfied with the quantity and quality of the nuclear weapons, reactors, and other devices developed by AEC laboratories and manufactured according to rigid specifications monitored by AEC and contractor staff.

The establishment of a special agency devoted primarily to the development and production of nuclear weapons resulted from the recognition that these were extraordinary weapons, not manufactured by conventional means and too fearful to be incorporated in the ordinary arsenal of the Armed Services for use under ordinary circumstances. There was also a feeling that, in the development of radically new weapons, the military were their own worst enemy, since, having constantly to be ready to fight with the weapons of the day, they tended to neglect those of the morrow. As the wartime Office of Scientific Research and Development had demonstrated the fruitfulness of establishing a separate civilian agency to concentrate on the development of new military technology, it was natural enough to follow a similar model for the further development of the single most terrible of the new weapons.

The scientists who had devised the bomb and the chiefs of the military who had used it were in agreement that a civilian agency should control this new force,[1] although, from the early days to

[1] "The forces opposed to civilian control . . . never included the Military Establishment nor its principal chiefs, though of course they did include a few military individuals. More formidable than these few, though obviously in tacit or covert

the present, there have inevitably been disagreements about the precise line that should be drawn between the responsibilities of the civilian and military agencies. At the outset, General Groves made a case for the Army's retention of its stock of nuclear bombs and certain bomb production facilities, but, at Lilienthal's insistence, these were added to the list of properties transferred to the AEC on January 1, 1947.[2] Again, at a July 21, 1948, meeting in President Truman's office attended by the five Commissioners, Defense Secretary Forrestal, and the Secretaries of the Army and Air Force, Forrestal asked the President to transfer custody of the atomic bombs to the military—but Truman refused.[3] However, this was a legalistic issue as the bombs were, in any event, immediately available for use by the military upon authorization by the

---

alliance with them, were a certain segment of the press and certain forces behind it. . . ." W. W. Waymack, "Four Years Under Law," *Bulletin of the Atomic Scientists* (February 1951), p. 53. To be sure, the May-Johnson bill proposed by the Army in 1945 was regarded by many scientists as an effort to retain military control. However, such scientists as Bush, Conant, Oppenheimer, Fermi, E. O. Lawrence, and Karl and Arthur Compton helped to draft the measure, and General Groves has observed that "The only features of the bill that in any way permitted military participation in the proposed organization lay in the proviso . . . that military officers, active or retired, should not be barred from service either as members of the Commission or as its general manager." Leslie R. Groves, *Now It Can Be Told* (Harper and Bros., New York, 1962), p. 393.

As matters developed, no military officer has served on the five-man Commission. Officers have served in the post of general manager (though, in order to do so, they have had to retire from active service) and in many AEC divisions, particularly the Division of Military Application (whose director must, by law, be a member of the Armed Forces) and the Division of Reactor Development. Navy officials backed the final McMahon bill, as did General Eisenhower, then Army Chief of Staff, who was anxious to have the large atomic energy expenditures removed from the War Department budget. Nonetheless, after passage of the McMahon bill, "Dissatisfaction with civilian control continued to manifest itself [among "certain military interests"] through legislative proposals seeking in various ways to increase military participation in the atomic energy program. During 1947 and 1948, seven bills were introduced in Congress to this end." Morgan Thomas, *Atomic Energy and Congress* (University of Michigan Press, Ann Arbor, 1956), p. 45.

[2] See Richard Hewlett and Oscar Anderson, Jr., *The New World, 1939-1946* (Pennsylvania State University Press, University Park, 1962), pp. 643 and 651-52.

[3] Accounts of this meeting appear in Lewis Strauss, *Men and Decisions* (Doubleday & Co., New York, 1962), p. 160, and *The Journal of David E. Lilienthal*, op. cit., Vol. II, pp. 388-92.

President.[4] Since the early 1950's, weapons custody has been continually transferred to the military by the annual authorization of the President.

Despite the personal cleavage, and then hostility, that developed between Groves and Lilienthal, and numerous practical difficulties that arose in the course of transferring contracts, facilities, personnel, and power, this was the only dispute between the military and the AEC taken to the President for resolution from 1946 through 1949. In his first yearly report as Secretary of Defense, Forrestal stated, "I want to record my personal satisfaction with the existing statute governing matters in the field of atomic energy, and to express my pleasure, also, at the way in which relationships between the National Military Establishment and the Atomic Energy Commission are being conducted."[5] The Military Liaison Committee representing the Armed Services, established by the 1946 Atomic Energy Act, met alone periodically with the Joint Committee on Atomic Energy (which has regularly included on its rolls important members of the Armed Services committees of both Houses) and "expressed their full satisfaction in the way the liaison arrangement . . . was working out."[6] Mervin J. Kelly, Vice President of the Bell Laboratories, who examined the Los Alamos laboratory and allied nuclear installations in the spring of 1949, observed that relations between the Commission and the military had moved "from a situation that I would call rough and unsatisfactory to one that I would say is now [July 1949] satisfactory and is moving in the direction of being very good."[7] Again in March 1955, as chairman of the Hoover Commission Subcommit-

[4] Cf. the following exchange between Representative Chet Holifield and AEC Chairman Lilienthal on June 16, 1949: "Can you assure us, Mr. Lilienthal, . . . that, notwithstanding the fact that the Commission is in technical custody of the bombs, they are available instantly without undue delay of any type to the military in case there is need for them to take the bomb and deliver it?" "I can." *Investigation into the United States Atomic Energy Project,* Hearings before the Joint Committee on Atomic Energy, 81 Cong. 1 sess. (1949), Pt. 9, p. 420.

[5] National Military Establishment, *First Report of the Secretary of Defense* (1948), p. 16.

[6] Joint Committee Chairman McMahon on June 9, 1949 in *Investigation into the United States Atomic Energy Project,* Hearings before the Joint Committee on Atomic Energy, 81 Cong. 1 sess. (1949), Pt. 6, p. 262.

[7] *Ibid.,* Pt. 20, p. 814.

tee on Research Activities in the Department of Defense and Defense Related Agencies, Kelly commended the excellent relations between the AEC and the DOD:

The subcommittee has examined the formal procedures and informal methods of cooperation of these organizations. The subcommittee has found a well ordered and effective formal framework. To be sure, it is somewhat cumbersome, but this is perhaps inherent in so large an operation in which so many organizations are involved. The informal working relations are intimate, direct, and effective.[8]

However, throughout these years, important elements of the military and their allies in the Congress and the country evinced dissatisfaction with what they regarded as the slow rate of nuclear progress. Barely three weeks after the AEC had taken over from the Army, the chairman of the Joint Committee, Senator Bourke Hickenlooper, was complaining to Forrestal "about a pacifistic and unrealistic trend in the Atomic Energy Commission."[9] The Defense Department subscribed to Ernest Lawrence's and Edward Teller's 1949 campaign for a major hydrogen bomb effort, and the Secretary of Defense Louis Johnson, backed by Secretary of State Dean Acheson, this time won President Truman's support in a second confrontation with Lilienthal in the White House on January 31, 1950.[10] The first campaign which Captain Hyman Rickover and other proponents of the nuclear submarine had to fight

[8] *Subcommittee Report on Research Activities in the Department of Defense and Defense Related Agencies,* Prepared for the Commission on Organization of the Executive Branch of the Government by the Subcommittee on Research Activities in the Department of Defense and Defense Related Agencies of the Committee on Business Organization of the Department of Defense (April 1955), pp. 71-72.

[9] See the entry for Jan. 22, 1947, in Walter Millis, ed., *The Forrestal Diaries* (Viking Press, New York, 1951), p. 241.

[10] See Oppenheimer's October 1949 letter to James Conant: "Ernest [Lawrence] spoke to [Senator] Knowland and McMahon [both of the Joint Committee], and to some at least of the joint chiefs. . . . The joint chiefs appear informally to have decided to give the development of the super overriding priority . . ." and Oppenheimer's further statement on April 16, 1954: "Dr. Lawrence came to Washington. He did not talk to the Commission. He went and talked to the joint congressional committee and to members of the Military Establishment" (*In the Matter of J. Robert Oppenheimer,* Atomic Energy Commission, 1954, pp. 242-43). The January 31, 1950 meeting with President Truman, and the meeting of the Special Committee of the National Security Council which preceded it that morning, are described in *The Journals of David E. Lilienthal, op. cit.,* Vol. II, pp. 623-34.

within the Navy was followed by a second which the Navy had to fight for acceptance of the program by the AEC.[11] The Air Force's threat to contract with the University of Chicago for a second nuclear weapons laboratory apparently finally induced the reluctant Commission to establish the Livermore laboratory in July 1952.[12] And the expansion of uranium procurement and nuclear production facilities in the early and middle 1950's can be attributed to pressure on the AEC by the military and the Joint Committee,[13] endorsed by President Truman. It was subscribed to by President Eisenhower also, who saw in a heavier reliance on nuclear weap-

[11] "The AEC accepted a Navy program. The difficulty was that the AEC did not accept as large a program as the Navy wanted," an AEC staff member observes. In an address on April 2, 1948, Rear Admiral Mills, head of the Bureau of Ships, complained of the AEC's indifference to nuclear submarines. At one point, Rickover threatened that the Navy would proceed to develop a nuclear power plant on its own. Evidently the Commission feared that diverting men and nuclear material to the submarine program would slow up production of atomic bombs. See Clay Blair, Jr., *The Atomic Submarine and Admiral Rickover* (Henry Holt and Co., New York, 1954), pp. 102, 108, and 112.

[12] After unsuccessful efforts in the winter of 1951-52 to persuade the AEC to establish a second weapons laboratory, Edwin Teller relates, "I took my recommendation that a second laboratory be established to David Griggs, chief scientist for the Air Force . . . a short time later . . . Griggs arranged for me to meet General James A. Doolittle. . . . [and subsequently, Secretary of the Air Force Thomas K. Finletter]. . . . Finletter flew to Los Alamos and verified for himself the importance of developing hydrogen bombs and my assessment of the areas in which more work could be done. Then he asked me to state my case before Secretary of Defense Robert A. Lovett. . . . Defense Secretary Lovett listened to the problem and . . . maintained that a second laboratory was, indeed, necessary to our security. The Air Force laid plans for a laboratory under its own jurisdiction and even began negotiating for a site. ["Investigating" a site might be more precise as, apparently, the Air Force's discussions with the University of Chicago did not proceed to the stage of contract negotiation.] Then the Atomic Energy Commission, at last, became interested and began investigating possible locations for a second laboratory." Edward Teller with Allen Brown, *The Legacy of Hiroshima* (Doubleday & Co., Garden City, N. Y., 1962), pp. 59-61.

[13] "On January 21, 1952, the Joint Committee received plans from the military whereby the proportion of the nation's defense dollar spent on atomic weapons might be increased. This was approved by the National Security Council on January 22. The Joint Committee kept prodding the AEC to submit a supplemental budget request, which finally was received on May 29. . . . The biggest single outcome of this program was the huge production facility at Portsmouth, Ohio. . . ." Morgan Thomas, *Atomic Energy and Congress* (University of Michigan, Ann Arbor, 1956), p. 108. The AEC did not oppose the expansion program, an informant notes, "but there was a hassle over the size of the budget."

ons for tactical as well as strategic purposes a way of defending Europe and increasing the nation's military power while economizing on military manpower and expenditures.[14] Secretary of State Dulles' enunciation of the "massive retaliation" doctrine in January 1954 put the public capstone on a policy formally adopted by Eisenhower and the National Security Council the previous October.

Three broad points should be made about the influence of the military on AEC policies and programs during the years when the demand for nuclear materials still exceeded their increasing supply: 1. The three services competed for nuclear materials, so that the AEC, the Administration, and the Congress were confronted with the problem of assigning relative priorities to the Air Force's demand for strategic bombs and a nuclear powered plane, the Army's demand for tactical weapons, and the Navy's demand for nuclear submarines. 2. Expenditures on nuclear forces competed in the overall defense budget with expenditures on conventional forces (which were, in the view of many, relatively downgraded until the advent of the Kennedy Administration).[15] 3. Military de-

[14] On October 30, 1953, President Eisenhower approved National Security Council paper 162/2, which stated that "the military services could plan on using nuclear weapons, tactical as well as strategic, whenever their use would be desirable from a military standpoint. . . . The intent of this decision was to foreclose any of the services—in particular the Army—from generating large requirements for manpower and conventional equipment. . . . There was to be no repetition of a conventional limited war on the scale of the Korean War, and no conventional 'general war.' Of course, the fundamental assumption behind the new directive was that the fantastic fire power concentrated in atomic weapons would reduce manpower requirements and overall costs." Glenn H. Snyder, "The 'New Look' of 1953" in Warner R. Schilling, et al., Strategy, Politics, and Defense Budgets (Columbia University Press, New York, 1962) , pp. 436-37.

[15] Cf. Glenn Snyder's analysis of the strategic debates of 1953-54: "The 'absolute priority' group which included most of the Air Force leadership, many of the top civilian officials, including the Secretary of the Treasury and the President [Eisenhower], himself, tended to argue that the requirements of the first priority (long-range air-nuclear power . . .) should be entirely fulfilled before any resources were allocated to lower priorities. The 'relative priority' group, led by the Army and the Navy, while recognizing the importance of an adequate retaliatory capability, asserted . . . that at some point before total requirements for this capacity (as stated by the Air Force) were reached, increments to surface forces began to assume greater (or equal) utility than further increments to air power." (ibid., p. 438.) The Oppenheimer hearings of 1954 provide extensive evidence of the conflict between the Air Force, which wanted to employ the available nuclear materials for making

mands delayed the advent of major programs to develop peaceful uses of nuclear technology, particularly in the field of civilian power and maritime propulsion.[16]

It is perhaps not strictly correct to refer, as we have done, to the Department of Defense as the AEC's best "client," since there is relatively little transfer of funds between the two agencies; "political supporter" would better describe the relationship, because the department's support and endorsement of specific nuclear programs have played so large a part in the past expansion of the Commission's budget. AEC may either fund the nuclear portion of a development program while DOD finances the non-nuclear portion (as was done with the nuclear propelled aircraft) or fund the entire cost of developing new prototypes while DOD finances the procurement of subsequent operational models (as has been the case with submarine nuclear reactors).

The extent to which DOD is prepared to pay out of its own pocket is a fair test of its interest in a piece of nuclear merchandise; and as pressure on the DOD development budget has increased in recent years, the department's interest in a number of AEC programs has noticeably waned. "The Defense Department is for every experiment until they have to begin to pay for it. As long as the AEC puts it in their budget, they are for it 100 percent," Senator John Pastore, chairman of the Joint Committee, has observed.[17] A number of observers have attributed the fabu-

bombs as big as planes could carry, and the Army and the AEC's scientific advisers, who favored assigning relatively more nuclear materials to smaller "tactical" weapons.

[16] "One military-civilian conflict arose in early 1955 over President Eisenhower's proposal for the immediate construction of an atomic-powered merchant ship. . . . Admiral Rickover . . . expressed the view that the merchant ship would result in the delay of the navy program . . . the Joint Committee, apparently fearing a drain of resources away from experiments on military propulsion reactors if the plan were carried out, voted not to authorize the peace ship. . . .

"There remains, then, a clear potential rivalry between the military reactor program and both civilian propulsion reactors and central-station power reactors. The clash of interest results from a competition in the Government's program for priority to employ the limited number of contractors and technicians capable of doing this work." Morgan Thomas, "Democratic Control of Atomic Power Development," *Law and Contemporary Problems* (Winter 1956), pp. 42-43.

[17] In *AEC Authorizing Legislation Fiscal Year 1965*. Hearings before the Joint Committee on Atomic Energy, 88 Cong. 2 sess. (1965), Pt. 2, p. 536.

lous hoard of nuclear weapons and materials in part to the fact that the Department of Defense simply accepted whatever production target the AEC could attain, since it did not have to foot the bill for it. If DOD actually had to pay the cost of producing these bombs and their nuclear ingredients by transferring funds to the AEC, they reason, it would balance the value of additional nuclear weapons against that of alternative military needs, and a more realistic weapons quota might emerge:

> . . . there would have been many fewer weapons designed and many fewer weapons produced if the money had come out of the relatively fixed ceiling on DOD funds. The result is, there is no incentive for DOD to be sparing on its nuclear weapons demands . . . the greatest beneficial restraint on the proliferation of nuclear weapons would come from making the Department of Defense budget for these weapons.[18]

Among the nuclear development programs that have been cut back or curtailed since 1961 due to decisions by the Secretary of Defense (with the backing of the President) were the nuclear propelled plane, the "Pluto" nuclear ramjet, and the nuclear powered aircraft carrier requested by the Navy in 1963. Advocates of nuclear technology have noted dourly that Harold Brown was more enthusiastic about some of this technology when he served as director of Livermore than after assuming his post as Assistant Secretary of Defense for Research and Engineering.[19]

As a result of these cutbacks, Representatives Melvin Price and Chet Holifield and Commissioner James Ramey have attacked the "requirements" system under which a user agency such as the Department of Defense must express a definite need for a new technical device before research and particularly development work can proceed to advanced stages. Such a system, they argue, serves to perpetuate conventional technology, since many potential uses of radically new technology cannot be foreseen until they are actual-

---

[18] From a July 1965 letter of a former high government official who had had full access to relevant classified information.

[19] "We do not have Dr. Brown's support for the SNAP 10-A, we did not have a very vigorous support for Rover from him, and we did not have a very vigorous support on the nuclear aircraft carrier with which we were greatly concerned." Representative Chet Holifield in *AEC Authorizing Legislation Fiscal Year 1965, op. cit.*, Pt. 2, p. 439.

ly demonstrated. They have therefore pressed for authority to have the AEC conduct such demonstrations. ". . . developers should carry promising developments through the demonstration stage, including flight test where aerospace activities are involved," Ramey has urged. "Each development project should have an 'objective' rather than a requirement. The objective should normally be stated in terms of achieving successful prototype tests in the appropriate environment."[20]

The attack on what Commissioner Ramey has characterized as the "requirements merry-go-round" has been linked with comparable criticism of the "cost-effectiveness" approach that Secretary of Defense McNamara and Defense Comptroller Charles Hitch instituted with the blessing of President Kennedy to help balance the merits of alternative military programs against their costs; which is to say, it has been linked with criticism of the budgetary restraints on nuclear technology. ". . . what counts in war is 'military effectiveness'—not 'cost effectiveness,' " declared Joint Committee Chairman Chet Holifield in criticizing the Defense Department (and especially Secretary McNamara) for not building more nuclear powered surface warships.[21]

This is a natural enough argument for a promotional committee and agency; but at one stage or another in the sequence of technical development, the tests of utility and/or economy must obviously be posed; and when the costs of development rise or the agency budget falls, that stage will necessarily come somewhat sooner. This is the unaccustomed situation in which many DOD-AEC programs have been put in recent years.

[20] James Ramey, "The Requirements Merry-Go-Round in Government Research and Development," address at American University, April 20, 1964.

[21] Remarks at keel-laying ceremony for U.S.S. *Narwhal*, Groton, Conn., Jan. 17, 1966.

Though, under the terms of the 1946 Atomic Energy Act, the AEC's General Advisory Committee of nine members serving part-time "from civilian life" was appointed by the President, the committee did not usually report directly to him, as Bush reported to Roosevelt, but to the Commission; then, too, there was the Joint Committee on Atomic Energy, which Bush had never had to contend with. Nonetheless, the GAC enjoyed great influence over the government's emerging nuclear policies. Members of the original committee were: Robert Oppenheimer, chairman; James Conant, Lee DuBridge, Enrico Fermi, Isidor Rabi, Hartley Rowe, Glenn Seaborg, Cyril Smith, and Hood Worthington. Four were physicists; two, chemists; one, a metallurgist; and two, engineers; seven were associated with academic institutions and two (Rowe and Worthington) with industry. Robert Bacher, the physicist member of the first Commission, had interpreted the Act's provision that the GAC should advise the Commission "on scientific and technical matters relating to materials, production, and research and development" to indicate that it should be composed of "chemists, physicists, metallurgists, and engineers,"[3] and this has remained its predominant complexion to date.

From the outset, the GAC endorsed the philosophy of operating by contract rather than in civil service laboratories, and strove to rebuild the morale of the AEC laboratories which had been damaged by the return of leading scientists to universities after the war. However, as eminent private citizens drawn from eminent private institutions, the GAC appears to have given less enthusiastic support to the growth of the AEC laboratories over the years than has, for example, the Joint Committee on Atomic Energy, preferring to see a relatively larger volume of R&D contracting at privately owned laboratories and being especially concerned to give adequate encouragement to basic research at universities. Thus, Oppenheimer observed:

There were arguments in those days [1947 and 1948] that the Commission was so short handed, so in need of physicists, that the best thing they could do was to make it hard for physicists to get jobs so that they would come and work in the various [AEC] laboratories. We [the General Advisory Committee] thought that was quite wrong—

[3] *Ibid.*, p. 648.

that the best thing they could do was to support physics in the universities. . . .

I think on this we probably pushed the Commission and they regarded us as people who were, after all, largely professors and university presidents and we were pleading a special interest. We did plead a special interest, but we believed it to be the national interest, too.[4]

The 1950-53 expansions of plant for the production of plutonium and uranium were, Gordon Dean said, "blessed by the General Advisory Committee." To the question, "Did they help to suggest and initiate expansion programs?" he replied, "It is very hard to put your finger on it. A need arises, and there are many huddles. Probably the records would show that some had originated with the GAC but on this I am not sure."[5]

The Commission's 1960 report on the future of its laboratories was noticeably equivocal about the proportion of R&D expenditures which the laboratories might expect to receive in years to come, and that which might go to private facilities. The sections of that report submitted by each laboratory, however, made it clear that, as a group, the laboratories looked for expansion in a variety of directions—indeed, that most were exploring as many directions as possible in the hopes that some, at least, would prove rewarding. In this context, the comments of the GAC on the Commission report appeared as a counsel of restraint, designed to keep laboratory budgets at their present or reduced levels:

We would not expect that the project engineering laboratories [Evendale, Bettis, CANEL, Knolls, and Sandia] with the exception of Sandia, would indefinitely have support from and be under the supervision of AEC. . . .

. . . in the long run it would be more appropriate for the support of . . . [the Argonne Cancer Research Hospital and the University of Rochester medical program] to come from the Department of Health, Education and Welfare. . . .

The Commission should be cognizant of scientific and engineering manpower needs in our total society. The AEC should not increase scientific and technical personnel on a project if such manpower is

[4] *In the Matter of J. Robert Oppenheimer*, Hearing, Personnel Security Board, Atomic Energy Commission (1954), p. 74.

[5] *Ibid.*, p. 301.

badly needed on other projects of higher technical priority for our welfare and security.

. . . when . . . a [major basic research] facility is provided at an AEC multiprogram laboratory, the laboratory should not build its staff to fully utilize the new facility, but should expect university scientists and engineers to make substantial use of the facility. . . .

We would be more inclined to restrict the size of the multiprogram laboratories than is indicated in the report. We believe that the effectiveness of the present laboratories can be improved better by emphasizing quality rather than size. . . . As new assignments are accepted by a particular laboratory, some of the less productive older programs should be eliminated. . . .

The more specific development projects based on concepts and technologies already available should be done under contract with appropriate industrial organizations. And the laboratories should not, of course, undertake any projects which industry is ready to carry out at its own risk and initiative.[6]

During the early years, the GAC did not confine itself to technical problems but branched out freely and volunteered advice on broad issues of national and international civilian and military nuclear policy. "What made you think that it was appropriate for you to speak about these rather nontechnical but more political, diplomatic and military considerations?" Rabi was asked in 1954. ". . . somehow or other," he replied, "we didn't feel it was inappropriate. In our whole dealing with the Commission, we very often, or most often, raised the questions to be discussed . . . we would say we want to discuss this and this thing. Would you please provide us with documents, would you bring individuals to us on this. . . . On the other hand, we didn't feel badly if they didn't act on our suggestions. Sometimes they did and sometimes they didn't." In 1949, Oppenheimer conveyed a similar impression of the GAC's activities; but asked if "The Atomic Energy Commission has followed the recommendations which the General Advisory Committee has given them?" he answered simply, "Yes."[7] Com-

[6] The Future Role of the Atomic Energy Commission Laboratories, Joint Committee on Atomic Energy, 86 Cong. 2 sess. (Oct. 1960), pp. 244-46.

[7] See In the Matter of J. Robert Oppenheimer, p. 455; and Investigation into the United States Atomic Energy Project, Joint Committee on Atomic Energy, 81 Cong. 1 sess. (1949), Pt. 7, p. 293.

menting on this period recently, National Academy of Sciences' President Frederick Seitz went so far as to say that "it wasn't clear whether the Commission or the General Advisory Committee ran the organization."[8]

This era of GAC glory ended in the early 1950's after Truman overruled the GAC-Lilienthal recommendation against a big hydrogen bomb program. With the installation of the Republican administration in 1953 and Eisenhower's appointment of Lewis Strauss not only as AEC chairman but as his special assistant for atomic energy, Edward Teller and the dissident scientists whose views the GAC had rejected gained a more direct line to the Commission and the White House than the GAC.[9] Their victory, presaged by the GAC's and Commission's reversal in the summer of 1952 of earlier, repeated opposition to a second nuclear weapons laboratory, was reinforced in 1954 by the branding of Oppenheimer as disqualified for further government service. It may be recalled that the favorable testimony given at the Oppenheimer hearings in April and May 1954 by nine former or current members of the GAC (including Conant, Fermi, von Neumann, Fisk, DuBridge, and the then chairman, Rabi), General Groves, five of the six former Commissioners (including the two previous chairmen, Lilienthal and Dean), Vannevar Bush, Karl Compton, James Killian, and other of the nation's most eminent and, in other respects, influential spokesmen for science was of no avail against the less favorable testimony of one general and a few security officers and scientists—and, a number of people felt, of Oppenheimer himself. The dissatisfaction of scientists was not reduced by what they regarded as security excesses during the period of Strauss' chairmanship, 1953-58.

In policy terms, the removal of Oppenheimer from the Wash-

[8] See *A Bill to Amend the National Science Foundation Act of 1950*, Hearings before the Subcommittee on Science, Research, and Development of the Committee on Science and Astronautics, U.S. House of Representatives, April 19, 20, and 21, 1966, p. 102.

[9] "With the support of AEC Chairman Lewis Strauss, the influence of Edward Teller . . . became strong in the Administration . . . his scientific opponents were able to voice their arguments only at the lower level of the General Advisory Committee and in the relatively ineffective Science Advisory Committee which was still in the Office of Defense Mobilization" (Gilpin, *op. cit.*, p. 13).

ington scene represented at least a short-term triumph for the Air Force-Dulles doctrine of "massive retaliation"[10] over the GAC's advocacy of more balanced military forces and strategy. Although Strauss took more than one significant step to mollify the scientific community (arranging the appointment of von Neumann in March 1955 as the second scientist member of the Commission), these did not end the hostility of many nuclear scientists to his policies, as was demonstrated during the 1959 Senate hearings to confirm Strauss as Secretary of Commerce, when the Council of the Federation of American Scientists voted 25 to 1 against his confirmation. David L. Hill of the FAS then declared that Strauss

. . . has, through his previous official positions, substantially diminished the enthusiasm of scientists for association with Government work, destroyed the original high standing and prestige of the Atomic Energy Commission, injured the prestige of the United States in the eyes of other nations.

. . . The healthy interaction between scientific opinion and Commission policy was shattered. Events . . . occurred which shocked, dismayed, and humiliated the scientific community.[11]

With Eisenhower's appointment of James Killian as his science adviser in November 1957, and the concomitant elevation of the Office of Defense Mobilization's Science Advisory Committee to

[10] "This country's senior scientific weaponeers—with some exceptions—believe the Air Force 'destroyed' Dr. J. Robert Oppenheimer. . . . It can be stated that this view is widely held and that there is grave alarm about its ramifications among men of science who have worked on weapons and consulted on war plans since the days of the Office of Scientific Research and Development. . . ." Nat S. Finney, "The Threat to Atomic Science," *Bulletin of the Atomic Scientists* (September 1954), p. 285. This view derived some credence from the testimony of Air Force Major General Roscoe Wilson and former Air Force chief scientist David Griggs at the Oppenheimer hearings (see *In the Matter of J. Robert Oppenheimer, op. cit.*, pp. 679-97, 742-70).

[11] See *Nomination of Lewis L. Strauss,* Hearings before the Senate Interstate and Foreign Commerce Committee, 86 Cong. 1 sess. (1959), pp. 363 and 430-31. To be sure, the hostility which many scientists bore to Strauss and/or his policies (the distinction is, unfortunately, often difficult to make) was matched by the approval of many others, including such men as Niels Bohr, Norris Bradbury, Detlev Bronk, Lord Cherwell, Richard Courant, Leland Haworth, Mervin Kelly, Kenneth Pitzer, Edward Teller, Alan Waterman, Alvin Weinberg, John Wheeler, and Eugene Wigner (*ibid.*, pp. 1055-61 and Strauss, *Men and Decisions, op. cit.*, pp. 391-92 and 451-52).

the status of the President's Science Advisory Committee, a group of scientists similar (in stature, professional background, institutional affiliation, experience in nuclear affairs, and political moderation) to those on the GAC[12] again gained a strategic and confidential vantage point in the determination of national policies for nuclear science and technology.

The political advantage of confidentiality should be noted. Lewis Strauss remarked in 1959 that

> . . . the General Advisory Committee . . . has never been required to open its executive minutes and discussions to Congress so far as I am aware, or had not up to the date of my retirement on June 20 last; and I do not believe that such a committee would long continue to serve were it required to do so, or that freedom of discussion and good advice could be obtained from any group of men worth their salt under these conditions.[13]

However, few secrets remained in the major policy positions of the GAC and few in the personal life, character, and policies of its first chairman after publication of the 1954 Oppenheimer hearings— as few remained for Strauss after the grueling hearings on the confirmation of his appointment as Secretary of Commerce to which his (and, to some extent, President Eisenhower's) political enemies subjected him in 1959. As there is no policy without a weakness and no character without a flaw, it is not too difficult, in the course of such intensive scrutiny, to search out both and (rightly or wrongly) attribute the failings of a policy to those of its proponent's character. To open executive deliberations to the scrutiny of the Congress may either invite political attack or dilute the content of the deliberations so as to forestall it. When in 1960 AEC Chairman Seaborg "pledged that he would keep the [Joint Committee] . . . informed on pending matters . . . and, specifically, that he had no reservations about making reports of the General Advisory Committee available . . . ,"[14] one could almost infer either that the most delicate aspects of the GAC's advice were not re-

---

[12] Indeed, at least eleven men have served at one time or another, and occasionally at the same time, on both the GAC and the Office of Defense Mobilization's or the President's Science Advisory Committee.

[13] See *Nomination of Lewis L. Strauss, op. cit.*, p. 797.

[14] Green and Rosenthal, *op. cit.*, p. 101.

corded, or that the scope of its concerns had been narrowed as scientists' views about the nation's nuclear policies were conveyed through other channels in which advice was still held in confidence.[15]

With the establishment of the Office of Science and Technology in 1962, whose director was free to testify before congressional committees about matters other than his private advice to the President, Congress again breached the perimeter of the Executive's highest scientific counsels. However, many inner lines of defense remained intact, and we may expect the battle between congressional efforts to obtain access and executive efforts to maintain privilege to continue as long as our form of government.

The relative influence of the President's Science Advisory Committee (PSAC) and the GAC on nuclear programs has varied with the issue, the changing composition of each group, and changes in its relations with the President and the Commission. One informant believed that the influence of the GAC had grown in recent years, whereas that of PSAC had declined somewhat since President Johnson took office. He stressed, however, that the GAC remained strictly a technical advisory group to the Commission; it did not make policy or render advice directly to AEC laboratories; and it was the Commission which decided how to use that advice.

[15] Don Price has pointed out that Congress is not the only culprit in efforts to breach the confidentiality of scientists' advice to the Executive. The advisers have more than once been known to leak or otherwise publicize their advice, in an effort to win academic or public support for their position. "Too often . . . [the scientific adviser] is likely to want both the confidential ear of the responsible official and the right to tell the academic world all about that relationship. It is impossible to maintain at the same time the privilege of the confidential adviser, which is that of making an unpopular recommendation in private, and the privilege of the neutral scientist, which is that of communicating freely with his colleagues and the general public. . . .

". . . the Director of the Budget has become the head of the oldest and most influential staff agency to the President for one all-important reason: . . . no Congressman or columnist has ever been able to make an important political issue of the fact that the incumbent Director of the Budget had offered advice that the President failed to follow. Budget Directors have given critical and independent advice, but as confidential advisers.

"But this is not a role easy for a scientist to accept. His greatest weakness in such a role is his professional conscience, his feeling that he must be the spokesman for his scientific colleagues and for science generally." *Government and Science* (New York University Press. 1954), pp. 133, 181.

President Kennedy's appointment of Glenn Seaborg in March 1961 made a scientist chairman of the Commission for the first time. Since the appointment of Commissioner Leland Haworth the following month, also for the first time a majority of the Commissioners have had professional training in science or engineering, and a minority in law. Several accounts in the *New York Times* reported that a cleavage developed between the scientists and the lawyers on a number of policy issues:

Illustrative of this clash of philosophies was a dispute that went on for months over renewing the contract with the University of California for running three of the commission's national laboratories.

The scientists argued that in line with the principle of freedom of scientific research, a minimum of controls should be imposed on the university. The lawyers contended that if the commission was going to give the university $300,000,000 a year, the Government should exercise tighter controls over how the university and laboratories spent the money.

Another illustration was the debate last fall over the size of the commission's budget for the coming fiscal year. The two lawyers fought against any increase in the budget. The scientists are reliably reported to have expressed amazement that the lawyers should question the proposition that an ever increasing amount of money should be spent on scientific research.[16]

To such accounts Palfrey, a subsequent lawyer-commissioner, countered that "In the AEC when we examine a policy issue . . . I find no discernible difference . . . that can be traced to a scientist's or a non-scientist's viewpoint. . . . I was informed by the press that in the AEC, the scientists were lined up on one side and the two lawyers on the other. To my knowledge there has never been a decision of the Commission, certainly not during my time in office, in which there was a division of opinion with scientists on one side and lawyers on the other."[17] Outside observers may well exaggerate, as Commissioners may understate, the significance of policy differences that occasionally arise among Commissioners. This was as true in the early days of Lilienthal and Strauss as it seems to

[16] John Finney, "2 Non-Scientists Sought for A.E.C.," *New York Times* (July 1, 1962).

[17] John Palfrey, "Government, Science and the Distracted Scholar," address at the University of Maryland, Nov. 8, 1963.

have been in the more recent days of Olson and Haworth. And so, though some well placed informants affirmed the *New York Times* account,[18] others equally well placed dismissed it as highly distorted, because, if out of 2,000 decisions in four or five years divisions did arise in a few cases, "what does it mean?" They agreed that, with a majority of scientists, the Commission pushed certain pure research programs more, and certain development programs less, vigorously than would otherwise be likely, but saw no evidence that this had produced any significant internal policy cleavage.

Doubtless, the full-time university scientists serving the AEC or the President in a part-time advisory capacity have had a broad (not necessarily a personal) vested interest in strengthening basic research at universities, and, as Oppenheimer freely acknowledged, have used their advisory positions to promote that interest.[19] The point has been taken so much for granted it has been subjected to relatively little criticism: excellent university scientists are hardly expected to oppose excellent university science. The larger criticism that has been leveled at the role of the President's Science Advisory Committee in nuclear affairs has been directed at their larger function: the disinterested evaluation of the technological programs and proposals of vested industrial and governmental interests. (Disinterest is, of course, a relative matter; one would expect a committee of industrial engineers and executives to be more disinterested with respect to university basic research proposals than proposals for the development of industrial technology.)

PSAC and the Office of Science and Technology (OST) are also

---

[18] ". . . the cleavage . . . undeniably existed after September 1961. Much of the issue had its origin in . . . the rapidly increasing level of funds for basic research in high-energy physics and the education support programs" (letter, July 9, 1965).

[19] Cf. Alvin Weinberg: ". . . even the professor of purest intent must be in some measure loyal to the Estate which he represents. As a result, government scientific advisory circles tend to be preoccupied with science at the universities, rather than with science in industry or in government laboratories; the whole structure and cast of thinking is geared to the problem of university science, and the limitations of the university as an instrument of government are overlooked. It would not be a great exaggeration to describe the advisory apparatus of the scientific government as a lobby for the scientific university." "The New Estate," *Yale Scientific Magazine* (October 1963), p. 16.

so placed that, like the Bureau of the Budget, they must be relatively less concerned with the special interests of any one agency than with the broader national interest, insofar as the two can be separately distinguished and defined. Exercising this function, they have inevitably exerted a restraining influence on certain programs of nuclear development, and thereby aroused the hostility of the Joint Committee and other persistent advocates of nuclear technology. "I'm not a great admirer of OST," remarked one influential advocate of this technology. "Every time you go to them, they hurt, not help." OST "has become a mechanism to pool responsibility, and for delay," said another. ". . . instead of breaking technical bottlenecks and helping to get things started and accomplished, the [President's] Science Adviser apparently became a sort of 'super-no-man' in league with the Bureau of the Budget," Representative Melvin Price complained in a forceful address in which he attacked the composition, secrecy, and judgment of PSAC:

The members of [PSAC] . . . can go out and make speeches and appearances of various sorts to create a favorable image for their views. But their reports are kept secret—not on grounds of security—but on grounds of privilege. . . .

We need a more diversified selection of scientific advisers. For example, the AEC's General Advisory Committee does not have a person with a medical or biological background on it. There also seems to be a concentration of scientific advice from big business, and big universities. The only way to dispel criticisms that our scientific advice is monopolized by one or more cliques is to demonstrate that we do not have them. . . .

. . . some of our scientists and administrators in the atomic field may be losing their pioneering spirit. Many of these achieved their reputations a number of years ago and are getting older in scientific counsel as well as in other ways. . . .

In obtaining a diversified group of scientific advisers for the President and the Agencies, I hope we can get some 'doers.'[20]

In the view of the Joint Committee, the White House science advisers helped to kill the aircraft nuclear propulsion program and to slow the pace of programs to develop civilian nuclear

[20] Melvin Price, "Atomic Science and Government—U.S. Variety," remarks before the Washington, D.C. chapter of the American Nuclear Society, June 14, 1961.

power and the use of nuclear technology in outer space. The preference of academic scientists for pure research, on the one hand, or for far-out technology on the other, Commissioner Ramey has argued, has led them to neglect projects offering more modest but practicable technical advances, with the strange ultimate consequence that the scientists actually perpetuate conventional technology:

Many scientific advisers . . . have not had experience with or understanding of engineering development. . . . One type is usually against going ahead with any development project to the hardware stage. The other type seems to have a predilection for advanced or exotic developments . . . this tendency either to do nothing or to force atomic energy hardware development into uncertain areas of technology . . . tend[s] to favor the established conventional technology.[21]

These criticisms are in part warranted, and some scientists, at least, have acknowledged their mistaken technical judgments about development programs such as the hydrogen bomb and the nuclear submarine.[22] But, one suspects, public attacks on the President's advisers are often a way of avoiding direct attack on the man who set them their task and was responsible for acting on their advice: the President. Particularly on budgetary matters (and budgets are always an issue in program choices), the voice of the President sounds louder and clearer in the Executive Office of the President than it may on the Hill.

[21] James Ramey, "The Requirements Merry-Go-Round in Government Research and Development," remarks before the Ninth Institute on Research Administration of the American University, Washington, D.C., April 20, 1964; see also Ramey's address, "The Requirements Merry-Go-Round—Phase II," before the Atomic Industrial Forum, San Francisco, Dec. 2, 1964.

[22] For example, Hans Bethe has acknowledged that in "the case of the nuclear submarine . . . I and many other scientists were bad prophets. None of us could understand why the U. S. was developing it: It was much more expensive than an ordinary submarine, and we didn't see why the United States was so much interested in submarines anyway, because we had the command of the sea on the surface." "The Social Responsibilities of Scientists and Engineers," a Nov. 6, 1963 lecture reprinted from *The Cornell Engineer* (December 1963), by the Council for a Livable World (Washington, D.C., 1964).

CHAPTER XI

Industry

Private industrial organizations have received the bulk of AEC expenditures and also the bulk of those devoted to research and development, though only a fraction of the large and increasing expenditures for basic research.

Two predominant features have characterized the AEC's relations with private industry: particularly in the early years, few firms were directly involved; and these operated under contractual terms muting many normal business incentives. To ensure military security and technical reliability, only a few "blue ribbon" companies were asked to undertake nuclear work; admission to the small circle of nuclear industry was not merely by invitation but, in important cases, by entreaty.[1] Essentially, the bargain that was struck was one in which private managerial and technical reputation and experience were exchanged for the government's assumption of all the costs, including protection against liability in the event of nuclear accidents. At little or no expense other than the diversion of significant management time and talent from commercial ventures, the chosen few firms obtained otherwise unobtainable knowledge about a remarkable new technology, some

[1] Cf. the remarks of Crawford Greenewalt, President of Du Pont: ". . . it has been the Government knocking on our door rather than vice versa. So that, for example, we had to be urged to assume the Savannah River project. It was a major undertaking that we certainly were not seeking. . . . This whole business of how one gets a Government contract, if one wants it, is not anything with which I have experience." Testimony, May 11, 1960, in *Organizing for National Security*, Hearings before the Subcommittee on National Policy Machinery of the Senate Government Operations Committee, 87 Cong. 1 sess. (1961), Vol. 1, p. 503.

portions of which might later prove commercially profitable. However, property rights, patents, and, in many cases, profits or fees were foresworn. As Truman told Senators Connally, Vandenberg, and Lucas at a September 1945 meeting during which he outlined his plans for atomic energy legislation, "This was too important a development to be made the subject of profit-seeking."[2]

Many private companies whom the Army or the AEC approached to undertake nuclear work in the early years of the program agreed. Seaborg and his fellow discoverers of plutonium had abbreviated the new element Pu instead of Pl to indicate its less pleasant aspects.[3] Scientists were not alone in this opinion; some of the staunchest capitalists and their allies in the Congress recognized that fissionable material must not be produced and merchandised freely, like chewing gum or lead; that here, if anywhere, private ownership and enterprise must be restrained, to safeguard, if not the nation's investment, then its defense and health, and to enhance prospects of international control. This attitude was reflected not only in provisions of the 1946 legislation which some of its supporters frankly characterized as "socialistic" or "totalitarian,"[4] but also in the terms of the contracts under

[2] Harry S. Truman, *Memoirs* (Doubleday & Co., Garden City, N.Y., 1955), Vol. 1, p. 529.

[3] One physicist familiar with this baptism writes, "This is an 'inside joke' among workers in this field. Actually, Pu as the abbreviation (or chemical symbol) for plutonium is in entire accord with the traditions of chemical nomenclature. Nearly half of the two-letter symbols for elements derive the second letter from other than the second letter of the name. The symbols starting with the letter P are: P (phosphorus), Pa (protactinium, Pb (lead, lat. plumbum), Pd (palladium), Pm (promethium), Po (polonium), Pr (praseodymium), Pt (platinum), Pu (plutonium). Pl would not be desirable as a symbol because it is not distinctive enough; too many elements have in their names the letter combination P,l."

Our version reflects that of Seaborg, who noted on one occasion that in ". . . the matter of a symbol . . . propriety was overruled. We chose 'Pu' for the reason you would suppose—rather than the more proper 'Pl.' Experience with the ornery element has proved our choice of 'Pu' to be most descriptive"; and, on another, ". . . while the symbol might have been 'Pl,' we liked the sound of 'Pu'—for the reason you might suspect." See "Plutonium: The Ornery Element," address at Richland, Wash., April 3, 1964, and "Room 307, Gilman Hall—Some Reminiscences," address at Berkeley, Feb. 21, 1966, reprinted in the *Congressional Record,* daily edition (April 15, 1964), p. A1878, and (Feb. 24, 1966), p. A961.

[4] For example, Congresswoman Claire Booth Luce, who supported the legislation, referred to it as "totalitarian" and "socialistic. . . . Some sections . . . might have

which leading corporations assumed responsibility for the management of government plants and laboratories. General Groves records that

Du Pont refused to accept our first letter of intent [issued on December 1, 1942] because it contained the standard [Army Engineer] proviso that, in addition to being reimbursed for costs, it would receive a fixed fee to be computed in accordance with the usual governmental procedures. Mr. [Walter] Carpenter [the company president] said that du Pont did not want any fee or profit of any kind for this work, and wanted furthermore to be certain that the company would receive no patent rights.[5]

Similarly, General Electric initially received only a $1 fee for the management of Hanford; and to this day no fee is paid to Western Electric for the operation of the Sandia laboratory.

However, it was not long after the end of the war that voices were raised from within the business community protesting the no-profit contracts.[6] "If the businessman takes the position that he can accept no more than a dollar a year profit for working on the atom, then certainly he is himself helping the Atomic Age to become also the profitless age . . . " an article in the January 1949

been written by the most ardent Soviet Commissar. Indeed, the patent provisions . . . are paralleled nowhere except in Soviet patent law. . . . A study of the Mc-Mahon committee's lengthy hearings will reveal how profoundly disturbed all the Members were by the socialistic implications of this unprecedented piece of legislation." *Congressional Record* (July 17, 1946) , p. 9261.

[5] Leslie R. Groves, *Now It Can Be Told* (Harper and Bros., New York, 1962), p. 58. Cf. Hewlett and Anderson's account of this episode: "The tremendous military potential of the atomic weapon posed a possible threat to the company's future public relations. The du Pont leadership had not forgotten the 'merchants of death' label slapped on the company during the Nye Committee investigations in the thirties. Certainly it was clear that the company had not sought the S-1 assignment; but, to keep the record straight, du Pont refused to accept any profit. The fixed fee was limited to one dollar. . . . Walter S. Carpenter, Jr., the du Pont president, disavowed not only profits but also any intention of staying in the atomic bomb business after the war. In his opinion, the production of such weapons should be controlled exclusively by the Government." *The New World, op. cit.*, p. 187.

[6] ". . . the report is in error when it states that some of the companies that have taken these operating contracts for $1 a year have not made a profit," one industry executive writes. "For example, [one contractor] . . . were probably making more money than they are now on a fee basis by being able to include a great deal of their corporate overhead." Letter, July 19, 1965.

issue of *Fortune* declared. "If, on the other hand, industry were to demand more profit from the atom—frank, open, fair, unashamed profit—and ask for less government-furnished capital goods, he might thereby begin to regain some of his old entrepreneurial spirit."[7] And former AEC chairman, David Lilienthal, returning to private life in 1950, protested the needless continuance of "the present airtight Government Monopoly of the industrial atom" and urged that secrecy be relaxed and a genuine private nuclear industry encouraged.[8]

As time has gone by, and particularly since passage of the 1954 Atomic Energy Act, there has been an evident trend toward "normalizing" AEC's relations with industry—that is, toward having them approximate, as much as possible, the ideal pattern of private industrial ownership, private pricing, free competition, and the risk of private funds for the possibility of private profit. However, the nuclear industry today, and for many years to come, will represent a strange modern version of that ideal:

An industry to which entry is by government permit, which requires government authority to construct its plants and acquire its raw material and fuel, which can sell its nuclear products . . . and its radioactive byproducts only to government licensees, which is subject to regulation of the price it may charge for its power output, which must license its main inventions and employ only licensed operators, is a far cry from the world of Adam Smith.[9]

The 1954 Act sanctioned private ownership of civilian power reactors producing fissionable material but not of the material itself, which was leased from the government; 1964 legislation required private ownership of nuclear fuels by 1973. When a private plant for reprocessing waste fuel from power reactors came into operation in April 1966 near Buffalo, the gaseous diffusion plants were the last major link in the chain of supply for a private civilian nuclear industry still in government hands, and suggestions have al-

---

[7] "The Atom and the Businessman," *Fortune* (January 1949), p. 162.

[8] See David E. Lilienthal, "Free the Atom," and "Toward the Industrial Atomic Future," *Collier's* (June 17 and July 15, 1950). Quotation from p. 14 of the latter issue.

[9] David Cavers, "The Atomic Energy Act of 1954" in *Atomic Power* by the editors of *Scientific American* (Simon and Schuster, New York, 1955), pp. 127-28.

ready been voiced for the eventual acquisition of one of these plants by private business:

> . . . perhaps as early as 1970, it should be practical for private enter-prise to take over the ownership and operation of a part of the existing capacity to supply commercial needs. When approximately 20 million kilowatts of atomic power utilizing enriched uranium is in existence or under construction in the United States, if the Government could find a way to sell a part or all of one of these [gaseous diffusion] plants at depreciated or book value, it should be practical for private enterprise to finance the undertaking and to operate at a profit at approximately the same prices as the Atomic Energy Commission charges. . . . I be-lieve it timely and urgent for private industry and the Atomic Energy Commission to look into the economics and feasibility of such a venture.[10]

The move toward private ownership has been accompanied by a liberalization of certain AEC contract provisions. Significant fees are now paid to all industrial operating contractors except Sandia and Du Pont.[11] "It has evolved into what you might almost call a normal commercial management and fee operation rather than a patriotic or exploratory effort in a new field of science," Congress-man Holifield remarked in 1962 of the General Electric contract at Hanford,[12] and the same could be said of most other operating contracts. In that year, fees for managing major AEC facilities ranged from 1 to 4 percent of the applicable operating costs upon which the fee was computed.[13] Indeed, what some people call a fee but others, a "management allowance" has for a good many years been included in AEC contracts with the Universities of Chicago

[10] K. D. Nichols, "Free Enterprise Aspects of Atomic Energy," an address before the Research Committee of the National Association of Manufacturers, Sheraton East Hotel, New York, April 24, 1964, in *Private Ownership of Special Nuclear Materials, 1964*, Hearings before the Subcommittee on Legislation of the Joint Committee on Atomic Energy, 88 Cong. 2 sess. (1964), p. 458.

[11] However, Du Pont does receive an allowance for central office administrative expenses associated with the management of the Savannah River plant; in 1962 this came to slightly over $1.1 million. (See *Systems Development and Management*, Hearings before a subcommittee of the House Government Operations Committee, 87 Cong. 2 sess. (1962), Pt. 5, p. 1668.

[12] See *ibid.*, p. 1662.

[13] *Idem.*, p. 1663.

and California.[14] But AEC fees have remained lower than those of the Department of Defense and the National Aeronautics and Space Administration, particularly in large contracts, for they have followed curves in which the fee declines proportionately more, as the size of the contract rises, than DOD and NASA fees. Industry has sought to raise them, and, in general, to get the AEC to adopt the more generous DOD policies with respect to patent rights, technical drawings, and recognition (in overhead) of the cost of proposals and of independent industry R&D. As a 1962 report of the Atomic Industrial Forum declared:

The present low fee schedule for AEC contractors performing research and development . . . and the failure to include as reimbursable costs substantial portions of the costs of doing business, all result in a very small profit incentive for private organizations to conduct Commission work. . . . Because of the lengthened time scale for the development of a commercial atomic energy business, the incentive now to conduct work at a low profit for the sake of future position is very much decreased. In addition, much of the Commission's research and development . . . does not differ from, and in many respects is competitive with research and development being contracted by [DOD and NASA] . . . it is not realistic, in an economic system based on the profit incentive, to expect indefinitely that front rank technical and manage-

[14] A "management allowance" was first incorporated in the AEC contract with Associated Universities in 1952 and subsequently introduced into other university operating contracts. During negotiations on the Argonne contract for fiscal year 1962, the University of Chicago requested a management allowance of $1.6 million, whereas AEC accountants put identifiable administrative expenses at $600,000; the figure was compromised at $1.2 million. See "A.E.C. Liberalizes University Fees," *New York Times* (Nov. 8, 1961). In fiscal year 1962, the University of California received an allowance of $2,150,000 for its expenses in managing the Berkeley, Livermore, and Los Alamos laboratories. Commenting on the Chicago allowance, Seaborg observed that "even though an institution like the University of Chicago is a nonprofit organization overall, this does not mean that there are not parts of its operation where profit accrues . . ." *Public Works Appropriations for 1963,* Hearings before a subcommittee of the House Appropriations Committee, 87 Cong. 2 sess. (1962), Pt. 6, "Atomic Energy Commission," p. 46. Former Commissioner Olson was blunter, declaring that "The University of California and the University of Chicago are, by the standards of the AEC's controller, at least, making at least a half a million dollars a year profit. . . ." Remarks at a forum of the Federal Bar Association 1963 Annual Convention, Sheraton Hotel, Philadelphia (Sept. 25, 1963). University officials, it need hardly be added, do not agree.

rial personnel will continue to be available for work which offers the contractor less opportunity for profit than alternative endeavors . . .[15]

A similar viewpoint was presented by Donald Peyton, Secretary of the Science and Technology Committee of the U. S. Chamber of Commerce, in commenting on the present study:

Examination of the allowable cost and unallowable cost provisions of Atomic Energy Commission contracts . . . will demonstrate conclusively that a substantial amount of those ordinary prudent business expenses requisite to the operation of a corporation in the United States is not allowed. . . . In addition, the Commission . . . until very recently . . . [refused] to pay any part of the expenses identifiable as bid and proposal expenses and independent research and development expenses. The Commission has recently changed its position on these two items (but only to the degree that a contractor can recover small amounts of these expenses). . . .

. . . even fixed price contracting with the Atomic Energy Commission, as well as some other government agencies, no longer represents the profit potential which should exist in the competitive market place. The Commission . . . is armed at the negotiating table with the right to secure the certified cost data and is armed at the completion of the contract with the right to re-examine it and to unilaterally reduce the contract price if its auditors should determine that the course of action is appropriate.[16]

As an unclassified, civilian nuclear industry began to emerge in the 1950's, a number of groups were established to clarify the interests of the industry and to convey them to the government. The largest and most representative was the Atomic Industrial Forum, formed in 1953 as the result of private initiative endorsed by Commissioners Keith Glennan and Gordon Dean. In addition to informational functions, fulfilled through annual meetings and a monthly publication, Forum committees and staff have surveyed and reported to the AEC and the Joint Committee industry views of government policies, and have conducted a number of detailed, careful, and influential studies on emerging policy choices. One observer suggested that the role thereby assumed by the Forum,

[15] *Report of the Ad Hoc Committee on Atomic Policy of the Atomic Industrial Forum*, Atomic Industrial Forum, New York (March 1962), p. 25.
[16] Letter, July 19, 1965.

and assigned to it by the Commission and the Joint Committee, may dampen the range of effective policy choice open to the government; he criticized the AEC, in particular, for tending to regard Forum studies "as an adequate substitute for external scholarly research."

While the Forum has not itself taken positions on legislation, it has organized committees which have submitted comments on, and proposed drafts of legislation, procurement regulations, and contract clauses of concern to industry, such as the reimbursement of industry R&D costs, the acquisition of patent rights, technical drawings, and nuclear insurance. However, as the Forum includes among its members representatives of trade unions and of universities and other nonprofit institutions engaged in nuclear work, it has drawn back from more forceful kinds of political lobbying which have been conducted, instead, by special nuclear committees of the Chamber of Commerce and the National Association of Manufacturers. For example, when a replacement was sought for Commissioner Robert Wilson, a former industry executive who resigned from the Commission in 1964, the NAM and the Chamber recommended candidates, but the Forum declined to do so, because, as one informant put it, ". . . that is a little too close to the [political] fire."

Relations between private industry and the AEC have, on the whole, been amicable. "There's a big alumni of the AEC out in industry, and we have very positive feelings about the Commission and what they're trying to do," said one industry representative. ". . . the nuclear-power business . . . has grown up under hothouse conditions, nurtured by government favoritism and subsidy," *Fortune* has noted. "So great is this dependence that one close observer . . . [remarked], 'Every time the AEC burps, the industry excuses itself.' "[17] Some industry spokesmen have been critical of what they regard as the excessive emphasis on pure research since 1961 by the Commission's scientific majority, and of the "competition" of AEC laboratories. By and large, though, they speak respectfully and favorably of the objectives and attitudes of the Commissioners and of senior AEC staff, reserving their harsher criti-

[17] "The Growing Market for Nuclear KW," *Fortune* (July 1963), p. 175.

cism for more junior staff who may be accused of being "bureaucratic," less interested in promoting free enterprise,[18] or trying to direct contractor programs into paths which (industry believes) they are not qualified to determine. Industry appears broadly satisfied with the direction AEC policy has been moving in recent years, recognizing that the pace of this movement is governed not by the AEC alone, but by broader national and international political considerations. Industry seeks simply, as one informant put it, "to keep the pressure on."

Beneath this stance of harmony a good deal of caution and, at times, fear can be discerned on the part of firms whose success or failure is, in the last analysis, highly dependent on the judgments and actions of the AEC and the Joint Committee. "Industry's 'positive feelings' about the AEC (and the . . . [Joint Committee]) are based as much on fear as they are on respect or admiration. There is an unusual concern about retaliation for criticism or bucking the established order," one reader declared.[19] Perhaps "as much" puts the matter too strongly; but that fear of— or healthy respect for—the Commission and the Joint Committee prevails among many persons in the nuclear industry can be confirmed by repeated evidence received in the course of this study.

[18] "Although the policies of the Commission itself are clearly in accord with the free enterprise clauses of the Atomic Energy Act and BOB 60-2 [Bureau of the Budget Bulletin 60-2, Sept. 21, 1959], it appears that the AEC's staff and organization is more strongly orientated toward the achievement of the other operating and regulatory objectives of the Act, than it is toward this promotional objective," declared the U. S. Chamber of Commerce's Task Force on Increasing the Role of Private Industry in the Government's Atomic Energy Program (undated recommendations ca. December 1960, released by the Chamber on March 21, 1961).

To this, Acting Commission Chairman John Graham replied that ". . . under the Atomic Energy Act the Commission's primary objectives must be the development and production of weapons and the conservation of dollars. Of course, this does not mean that the Commission is not strongly interested in implementing the free enterprise policies of the Federal Government in every way possible" (letter of Jan. 27, 1961).

[19] Letter, July 1965.

Present Roles and Motivations of "Dramatis Personae"

BY AN ANONYMOUS OBSERVER

The following comment on Part II of the draft manuscript of this book was received in October 1965. It is reproduced verbatim; a few editorial notes are inserted in brackets. H. Orlans

Joint Committee on Atomic Energy

The JCAE is the primary agency for setting the present objectives of the AEC. As has been discussed by many reviewers, it represents the leadership for the government's role in the atomic energy field.

The *first* concern of the JCAE relates to the weapons program and nuclear power for defense purposes. Because of their relationships to national defense, these areas have the least confusion in the government's program, with only an occasional conflict as a result of the JCAE's enthusiasm for atomic energy applications and the DOD's reluctance to embark on new developments in nuclear power (nuclear Navy, ANP [Aircraft Nuclear Propulsion], Pluto [nuclear ramjet missile]). The contractors are rarely involved in these issues except when a major program cancellation is considered, in which case the roles are similar to that experienced in any national defense project.

The *second* major concern of the JCAE relates to the use of atomic energy and radioisotopes for the benefit of the public at large. Because such public use involves in our society the participation of and promotion by commercial industries, the JCAE has become involved in the dual objectives of stimulating such promotion and at the same time preventing either monopoly or duopoly. With due regard for these objectives, the JCAE has assumed the role of the enthusiastic protagonist for the field of nuclear applications to the point where it has, for many years, pushed the Executive branch, the AEC, and other agencies for stronger programs and positive accomplishments.

The Atomic Energy Commission

The AEC has subtly accepted the JCAE as its principal customer and critic, and generally has abrogated a major responsibility for leadership. Its principal motivation is to implement the directions of the JCAE in a manner consistent with its historical development and machinery.

In the *primary* area of national defense, the AEC has minimal conflicts because the objectives and criteria have been fairly explicit and agreed upon. Particularly in the field of weapons development where the AEC has had full responsibility, it has done an outstandingly successful job and has had an opportunity to exercise judgment and to exhibit tangible accomplishment. In this field there has been a minimum of interference by any of the other groups involved. To this day, the weapons program remains the firm anchor which gives the Commission a sense of security concerning its role on the national scene. Even though the mysticism surrounding nuclear weapons has long since been dispelled, the DOD has not yet pushed to absorb this area.

In the applications of nuclear power for defense purposes, the AEC has not been able to play a fully responsible role. Unlike the uniqueness of nuclear weapons, nuclear power applications have to compete with other power sources. In the specific cases of the nuclear Navy, the ANP, and the Pluto projects, the AEC did not have the responsibility for determining "cost effectiveness" of these applications. The AEC was limited to being the developer and supplier of equipment specified by the DOD, although the cost of these programs appeared on the AEC budget. In the case of both the ANP and Pluto programs, the AEC exercised no judgment concerning their utility and did not openly engage in an examination of their military role. Long before these programs were cancelled, it was quite obvious to those engaged in such military "cost effectiveness" analyses that their justification had disappeared. The naiveness of the AEC in this situation may well have been stimulated by the large budgets associated with these activities. When these programs were finally cancelled, the AEC assumed the role of the innocent maiden and the JCAE the role of the angry father.

This situation relative to the applications of nuclear power to national defense still continues. The key problem is the lack of participation by the AEC in the detailed "cost effectiveness" studies conducted by the DOD. A similar situation exists in the application of nuclear power to space for NASA. An almost parallel naiveness exists in both the space nuclear propulsion and space electric power fields.

In the *second* major area of the AEC's responsibility, the development of the peaceful uses of atomic power and radioisotopes, the Commission has had a clear responsibility which has been consistently supported by the JCAE. It has attempted to develop a technology for this area as rapidly as possible, utilizing both the national laboratories and industrial contractors. Its primary interest has been to achieve the most effective use of government funds to accomplish the specific technological and political missions in these areas. As a result, the Commission has utilized organizations and skills wherever they have been located. It is obvious, therefore, that the "haves" would become stronger and the "have-nots" would become weaker. This situation has given rise to the "duopoly" which exists today in atomic power.

The Commission has always recognized that its allocation of responsibilities and contracts in the area of atomic power could well determine the future industrial competitive position in this coming commercial field. While the Commission has given lip-service to promoting true competition, it has in fact never been willing to give up the strong industrial contractor with a good history of accomplishment.

The present duopoly situation has been abetted by the role of the private utility industry. When the Congress and the Executive branch both gave up the attempt to use atomic power as a means of fostering federally-owned power plants, it became essential for the Commission to utilize the large private utilities as a vehicle. These utilities are quite comfortable with the duopoly situation. In addition, because each utility has a responsibility to its stockholders to take the most conservative course with relation to capital investments, the natural result is a dependence upon the strong and traditional industrial supplier.

The JCAE, as well as the Commission, has recognized the nature of the problem associated with broadening the competition in atomic power. Neither group, however, has been willing to face the cost, management difficulty, or the political criticism which might be associated with a firm plan to develop an "nth" force. The impact of recent Commission policies [of contractor change and segmentation] in correcting this situation has so far been trivial.

A *third* role of the AEC, the support of basic research in the pure sciences, has been completely self-engendered. It has not had the support of the JCAE nor of the Executive branch. However, because of the historical makeup of the Commission, the GAC [General Advisory Committee], and PSAC [President's Science Advisory Committee], the Commission has been able to exercise sufficient prestige muscle to establish a substantial budget in the pure sciences. The original justification for this role was based on the fact that federal support of the pure sciences needed an agency vehicle which the AEC could provide. This justification, of course, no longer exists because of the formation of the National Science Foundation. However, by undertaking this role for many years, the Commission was able to support not only many university programs but also principally the national laboratories. Except for the two weapons laboratories, Los Alamos and Livermore, and the nuclear Navy labs, Bettis and KAPL [Knolls Atomic Power Laboratory], there is no longer any basic justification for the Commission supporting any of the others. The universities look upon the national laboratories as competition for pure science support, and industry looks upon the national laboratories as competition for applied science support. The Commission has covertly recognized the basic lack of rationale for the present national lab program. However, if it broadens the activities of these laboratories to make them more useful for a variety of national purposes, they fall more logically in the domain of the NSF rather than in the limited domain of the AEC. This situation may require resolution on a much higher level than the AEC alone.

Office of Science and Technology and the Bureau of the Budget

The role of the OST and the BOB is primarily to reduce present and future budgetary commitments. As a secondary matter, they critically examine the present programs for consistency and efficiency in program planning.

In performing this role, these two agencies generally oppose the creation of new programs which may be in the long range economic or political interests of the country. However, such long range national objectives can be presented and accepted by the President. Such programs as the Moon mission and the Desalting program have been established by Presidential fiat and become the responsibility of the OST and BOB to implement.

In the specific field of atomic energy applications, these two agences have had minimal interest. There appears to be no real present pressure for the development of new power sources or for the conservation of national energy resources. The continuity of the atomic energy program is determined more by the momentum on the public scene of the Commission's activities than by any real support from the President. The various "Reports to the President" which the Commission recently prepared to justify their program were clearly exercises in rationalizing already approved activities and were, in fact, obsolete in many policy aspects at the time of their publication. To the OST and BOB, the atomic energy program is unwanted but unavoidable.

Depending on the character of the Commission, the AEC has trimmed its programs and policies to relieve the budgetary pressures created by these two agencies. In the past few years, this has resulted in a constant decrease in the funds available to promote atomic power applications. This shrinkage has been further aggravated by the specific interest of certain Commissioners in expanding the high energy physics program sponsored under the basic research program of the AEC. Although the JCAE has recognized this situation, it has not had the prestige to overcome the combined pressure of the scientific community. This continuing shrinkage of R&D funds for atomic power applications tends further to cement the duopoly situation in the commercial side of the field.

The Nuclear Industry

Three types of industrial contractors form the main branches of the nuclear industry. The first is primarily concerned with marketing R&D capabilities.

In this area they perform very much as do the R&D contractors to
and NASA. The second industrial group is primarily concerned with ͟
a wide variety of nuclear services and instruments associated with the use aͱ
measurement of radioisotopes. The third group are the industrial contractors
concerned with the development of central station atomic power with the
eventual intent of establishing a commercial business in the sale of such power
plants to utilities.

The R&D-oriented contractors face problems with the AEC similar to those
faced with other government agencies and do not in fact represent a special
case. It is generally true that such contractors consider the national labs as
competition for their activities and are constantly bringing pressure on the
Commission to reduce such competition. An additional problem with the
Commission is that their R&D policies were inherited from the old Corps of
Engineers-Manhattan District days, and are not consistent with those of DOD
or NASA.

That portion of the nuclear industry concerned with instruments and
services faces the problem of removing the Commission from competition as
the industrial organizations develop. Since these services are of a nuisance
nature to the AEC, there has been no real difficulty in meeting the pressure
from industry. This area of transition from government services to private
industry has gone well.

The Commission's *biggest* problem is associated with the industrial development of central station atomic power. As indicated before, the desire for
successful accomplishment has driven the AEC to use only the largest industrial
companies, and the utilities to use their principal suppliers. The resultant
duopoly will be very difficult to change. In this area, the Commission has
shown a surprising weakness and lack of self-confidence in its own programmatic judgments. Specifically, the Commission has permitted the two major
industrial suppliers to push their technical approach as the principal approaches for the country. In spite of the technical superiority of the more
advanced concepts which the Commission supports in principle, the timing
of these developments will be primarily determined by the activities of the
duopoly. While the combined political strength of the JCAE and the AEC
could probably foster a strong national program not supported by the duopoly,
there is now no evidence that such strength of leadership will develop.

The result is that the Commission constantly speaks of promoting competition in this area but in fact always ends up by taking the most conservative programmatic steps—steps which have so far resulted in strengthening the
position of the duopoly. This situation will continue until such time as the
Commission can override the pressures of the utilities and the duopoly.

The Scientists

Because of the history of the atomic energy field, the scientists who created
and nurtured this development still maintain the role of high priests. As a

group, their basic motivations result in the utilization of the AEC to further basic science rather than applications for public use. This group is quite capable of exercising powerful leadership for the accomplishment of these aims.

The JCAE and several members of the Commission are fully aware of the special interests of the scientists. Nevertheless, the Commission itself contains several of these high priests and no one has yet challenged them publicly. Thus, a basic conflict exists between the interests of the JCAE in the applications of atomic power and the disinterest of the scientists in this same area.

In addition to the power of the scientific members of the AEC, a special set of circumstances has maintained the influence of the scientists in other government bodies. It is generally assumed that industry's engineers and applied scientists are disinterested in the national interest and are concerned only with the self-interests of their companies. On the contrary, it is usually assumed that faculties of universities are unbiased and capable of making wise national decisions. For this reason, the bulk of the membership of PSAC, the consultants used by the OST, and finally the membership of the Commission's own GAC are predominantly made up of university-based scientists. It is almost inevitable, therefore, that all these advisory bodies would magnify the role of science in the national scene at the expense of applied technology.

PART III

Final and Further Observations

CHAPTER XII

Conclusions and Recommendations

The principal conclusions and, where warranted, recommendations of this study may be summarized as follows:

Operating Contracts Have Worked Well

Judged by its technological and scientific accomplishments, the policy of relying exclusively upon contracting for R&D and managerial services appears to have worked well to date, and there are few immediately convincing grounds for converting any particular laboratory or plant to an intramural basis. However, the desirability of doing so should not be dismissed *a priori,* on ideological grounds, but should be reexamined periodically and pragmatically.

In five or ten years, a new situation may prevail when more nuclear R&D and industrial facilities are privately owned and large amounts of fissionable material are owned, traded, and perhaps even produced privately.[1] In such circumstances, public operation

[1] The AEC advocated private ownership of fissionable material as far back as 1953; however, the Joint Committee on Atomic Energy would not agree until 1964. The Private Ownership of Special Nuclear Materials Act of August 1964 requires all such material now leased by the government to designated utilization or production facilities to be privately owned by July 1973. Industry has already expressed interest in the purchase or lease of a government-owned gaseous diffusion plant no longer required for military purposes, when the increased demand for nuclear fuel may render such an operation profitable. See *Private Ownership of Special Nuclear Materials,* Hearings before the Subcommittee on Legislation of the Joint Committee on Atomic Energy, 88 Cong. 1 sess. (1964), pp. 301-02. Long before the

of a research laboratory, a metallurgical assay unit, a test reactor, or a nuclear power plant might prove desirable, if only to provide a source of independent information and technical competence requisite to discharge the Commission's responsibility of protecting the public health and safety, and to manage effectively its major development programs. In brief, the policy of operating exclusively by contract should be a policy, not a dogma.

A Quality Test for Operating Contractors

The new policy of critically reviewing rather than routinely renewing operating contracts was long overdue and might well be extended to the major laboratories operated by universities and incorporated groups of universities. But a policy of changing contractors routinely would be just as foolish as one of never changing them. What is called for is a serious, critical, and independent evaluation of contractor performance at a stage in the contract term that permits the solicitation of proposals (including a proposal from the existing contractor, where warranted) and an orderly transfer, if necessary.

The evaluation of R&D programs in midcourse can be singularly difficult ("success in R&D is easier to define than failure," one scientist observes), but it is, in fact, done constantly by interim signs of progress, the present status and promise of findings, and the standing and outlook of the men doing the work. The efficiency of production, service, and managerial operations can be judged more readily. The key judgments cannot, of course, be made by inexperienced men sitting at their desks and looking at pieces of paper; they rest on intimate and highly pragmatic experience with a contractor's performance.[2] The judgment of an inde-

growth of a commercial demand for nuclear fuel, the first AEC chairman, David Lilienthal, observed that leasing the Hanford and Oak Ridge works "to the private concerns now operating them under contract has much to commend it." "Toward the Atomic Industrial Future," D. E. Lilienthal, *Collier's* (July 15, 1950), p. 68.

[2] As, for example, when a weapons laboratory director says, "We can send a telegram to _____ and a part will be on the plane tomorrow. _____ will go out on the floor and call out a guy and get him to work on it right away. They're terrific."

pendent technical committee visiting the laboratory prior to the decision on contract extension might also prove helpful.

The mere threat of contractor change can be useful in stirring a sluggish contractor to fresh efforts, and there are at least some AEC laboratories where a fresh show of life would be welcome. If the purpose of contractor change is not merely to spread the goodies around during a thin period for the nuclear industry but to promote the vitality of AEC operations, then the AEC should conduct a special evaluation toward the close of each contract term and state explicitly that: given an outstanding performance, contractors can anticipate contract renewal; given a good performance, their request for renewal will be entertained competitively with other proposals; a mediocre performance will lead to termination of the contract.

Commission Policy Needs Clarification

To obtain a detached appraisal of the performance of operating contractors, it is desirable in most cases to supplement the judgment of the cognizant AEC field office with that of headquarters staff (including not only members of the responsible program division but one or more representatives of other divisions) and qualified private witnesses. Unfortunately, detachment is often predicated upon a lack of intimate knowledge; but the regional AEC staff have been so intimately familiar with, and accustomed to the sitting contractor that, more often than not, apparently, they have found it hard to advocate a change, preferring the ills they have to those they know not of. And their judgment was more apt to be predicated on administrative or financial than on technical or general policy grounds. The recent tendency of the five Commissioners to concern themselves directly with operating contract awards ensures that such policy considerations will be given adequate weight; but it also renders their decisions more vulnerable to a variety of exigencies. This danger could be reduced if the Commissioners would enunciate more clearly the policies that guide their decisions. Such a clarification would also help to dispel uncertainty and give to AEC and contractor staff needed guidance about the future direction of Commission policies.

Are the production facilities and weapons laboratories subject to or excluded from the policy? Are the laboratory and plutonium reactors at Savannah River omitted, though those at Hanford were not, and, if so, why? Can Westinghouse expect the same future as General Electric, and if not, why not? Under what circumstances will a sitting contractor be invited to submit a proposal competitively with outsiders, and how can his special position be discounted in the evaluation process? Under what conditions should an installation be segmented and how should the segments be demarcated? Should the performance of nonprofit and profit-making contractors be judged by different criteria? Answers to these and related questions would be useful at the present juncture.

Conflicts of Interest

The award of operating contracts to companies with a private investment in the nuclear industry renders more likely conflicts between a contractor's public and private interests which must, therefore, be guarded against even more vigilantly than in the past.

Multi-Institutional Management

In its effort to placate the discontent of some universities and of congressmen in their region, the AEC has sought to reinstitute at Argonne, and entertained for other laboratories and for the prospective 200-bev accelerator, a system of management by a nonprofit corporation established by groups of many academic institutions. Such management of unique national basic research facilities appears desirable insofar as it promotes equitable access by qualified scientists from throughout the nation, provided that the laboratory director retains the authority to make on-the-spot decisions necessary to optimize use of the facilities. Optimal use also requires a strong staff of resident scientists and technicians, who make substantial demands on available machine time; but efforts should be made to keep that time as low as is compatible with the efficient and productive use of the machine.

To ensure equitable access, it should be sufficient to have on the governing board of a laboratory trustees from a number of high quality institutions of different types (including liberal arts colleges and perhaps industrial firms, which are not usually included), regions, scientific approaches, and fields. It should *not* be necessary to put on the board men from so many institutions that it reads like a directory of the region's, or the nation's, graduate schools, of low as well as high quality. Such a board may be useful for public relations purposes and to elicit political support from many universities and congressmen; but it is not an efficient means either of management or representation. It is maintained in bylaws that trustees are not to (and affirmed, at the best laboratories, that they *do not*) act as representatives of their institutions; and that if they *did,* this would open a channel of appeal from management decisions about machine use which would render effective operation of the laboratory very difficult. Why, then, is it necessary to have so many institutions in on the act? In fact, the participation of many institutions appears meaningless (i.e., nonfunctional), the significant decisions being delegated to smaller committees, or may adversely affect the status of the laboratory and the quality of its work and staff.

Nor does it appear wise to extend multi-institutional management to laboratories with major programs of applied research and development whose effective execution requires a clear concentration of managerial responsibility and the power to act rapidly and flexibly. Earlier experience has also demonstrated the danger that a group of academic institutions may give greater priority to programs of pure, and less to applied, research than the government's interests may dictate.

The proliferation of multi-institutional organizations and the increased number of institutions participating in them can become self-defeating. As Albert Crewe, director of the Argonne National Laboratory, has observed:

If, in every case, one must protect the interests of the faculty by insisting on a multi-institutional management, we face the ultimate prospect of every university being a part of the management of every laboratory. Such a solution is obviously ludicrous.

Perhaps a better solution would be for the laboratories to have simpler management but for all operators of laboratories to be members of a National Convention which could establish and enforce the ethics of such laboratory management.[3]

Adoption of some such code governing access to major national basic research facilities, with procedures for appeal to a distinguished group of arbiters under the auspices of the National Academy of Sciences or the Office of Science and Technology, has much to commend it. The suggestion is worthy of further investigation.

The Paper Jungle

The growth of cost controls, uniform regulations, and detailed reporting requirements have proceeded to a point that contractors widely regard as excessive, expensive, and injurious to the efficiency of their work. Fighting red tape is like fighting the jungle's encroachment on cleared land; it must be slashed and burned repeatedly. There have been periodic battles against unnecessary paperwork in the AEC's past; another one should be fought now. To be effective, it must receive the backing of the Joint Committee, since the proliferation of reports can be attributed, in part, to the committee's omnivorous appetite for information.

Fuller R&D Competition

To encourage the growth of a private nuclear industry, a larger proportion of expenditures for the development of civilian power reactors should be allocated to industrial laboratories, and a smaller proportion to the multi-program laboratories. In general (and despite the difficulty of identifying and equating true costs), a fuller and freer competition for R&D funds should be promoted be-

---

[3] Albert Crewe, "Regionalism: Needs, Assets, Liabilities," remarks at Purdue University Symposium on Science and Public Policy (April 12-14, 1965), p. 4.

tween the national laboratories and private industry, to ensure that work is done by the best qualified groups. To facilitate this, industry groups should be given full and timely information on AEC, and AEC laboratory, program plans.[4]

Clearer Technical and Economic Objectives

The first draft of this study concluded that "Of all Commission programs, those devoted to civilian reactor development seem in most need of clearer definition, narrower objectives, better coordination, and firmer management." At the end of 1964, the Commission instituted a reorganization of its reactor development programs in an effort to deal with criticism of this sort. Subsequently, a number of complaints were voiced that the Commission was going too far in the other direction, over-controlling, over-engineering, and exercising excessive technical direction in its civilian reactor programs. Enough evidence is not yet available to indicate whether the Commission or some of its new critics are right at the present juncture.

What is clear is that the technical objectives of civilian reactor contracting cannot be dissociated from their economic consequences. Although it was not a function of this study to examine the AEC's economic objectives, it is obvious that the task of defining them is as essential as it is politically difficult. Hoping for a competitive reactor industry and scattering limited contracts around has not achieved it. A good many observers believe that the Commission must either concert its contractual policies and funds so as

[4] Reactor division staff comment (in August 1965) that: (1) "The Director of RD&T [Reactor Development and Technology] has initiated a program of more intensive planning aimed at early identification and better definition of reactor research and development needs. Such efforts should result in making an increasingly greater share of reactor research and development work susceptible of proposal solicitation." (2) "Another plan under consideration . . . is the periodic issuance of general invitations for proposals in areas of technology where the chief reliance in the past has been upon contractor initiated unsolicited proposals. This plan, if adopted, would hopefully have the effect of increasing competition and broadening participation by more firms being informed as to AEC needs and stimulated to submit proposals. . . ."

to promote genuine competition, or resign itself to the existence of a monopoly and regulate it.[5]

[5] Cf. the recent report of the Joint Committee that "urged the AEC to exercise care that cooperative industrial efforts are not fragmented to such a degree that no single industrial firm obtains the necessary competence to become a competition force in the field." *Congressional Record*, daily edition (Oct. 20, 1966), p. 27104.

". . . it is not yet clear how far the AEC is prepared to go in intervening to alter the structure of the industry. . . . Nor has any statement that has come from the AEC so far given a clear impression of what the AEC's concept of a competitive industry may be." "The Impact of the New Order," *Nuclear Industry*, Dec. 1965, p. 7.

CHAPTER XIII

Two Further Issues

This inquiry began with the objective of examining some of the broad public policy issues involved in AEC contracting for R&D and management services. Nonetheless, it has unavoidably been forced to confront still broader issues, since the objectives and methods of contracting cannot be understood without some knowledge of their historical and institutional context.

Two of the largest issues repeatedly thrust upon us in the course of the study will be discussed in this chapter: the AEC's role in high energy physics, and, beyond that, the future mission of the AEC laboratories. We hope only to open, not to close, discussion of these questions.

The AEC's Role in High Energy Physics

The first draft of this study foolhardily recommended that the high energy facilities at Berkeley, Palo Alto, Cambridge, Brookhaven, and Princeton be transferred to the National Science Foundation. The voluminous comment thus provoked from charter citizens of the nuclear kingdom may serve as a point of departure for a consideration of the issues involved.

High energy physics has become one of the most expensive fields of pure science; annual government expenditures for it have been projected to reach $490 million in 1978, including an estimated $280 million for a baby 200-bev and $800 million for an 800-bev accelerator.[1] In FY 1964, the AEC alone spent some $125 million

[1] See *High Energy Physics Program: Report on National Policy and Background Information,* Joint Committee on Atomic Energy, 89 Cong. 1 sess. (February 1965), p. 48.

for research and construction in this field, and other government agencies (primarily the National Science Foundation, Office of Naval Research, and Office of Scientific Research), at least another $44 million.[2]

The predominant role of the Commission has come about gradually and not entirely at its own initiative. A critical decision was made by the Executive Office of the President in the spring of 1959, assigning to the AEC responsibility for the construction of the Stanford linear accelerator. Earlier Stanford accelerators had been financed by the Office of Naval Research, and there is reason to believe that the university might have preferred to continue dealing with that agency. "The decision to place the responsibility in the Atomic Energy Commission," AEC Chairman John McCone has indicated, "was based on a determination by the Bureau of the Budget, and those within the Bureau who are concerned with government organization matters, that the Atomic Energy Commission had considerable responsibility in this field of high-energy accelerators and a high degree of competence, and therefore it was felt that it would be best to keep this whole area more or less concentrated in the hands of one agency."[3] This assignment was not greeted by McCone with unmitigated joy. Fearing that the accelerator's heavy costs might adversely affect the budgetary prospects of other Commission programs, he sought from Budget Director Maurice Stans assurance that this would not happen. Although the Almighty Himself might be reluctant to give such an assurance in perpetuity, the more transitory budget director, on one reading, eventually volunteered it.[4]

[2] The $44 million expenditures of other agencies did not include capital costs. See *High Energy Physics Research*, Hearings before the Subcommittee on Research, Development, and Radiation of the Joint Committee on Atomic Energy, 89 Cong. 1 sess. (March 1965), pp. 780, 782.

[3] *Stanford Linear Electron Accelerator*, Hearings before the Subcommittee on Research and Development and the Subcommittee on Legislation of the Joint Committee on Atomic Energy, 86 Cong. 1 sess. (July 1959), p. 10. It is evident from these hearings that not only Budget Director Maurice Stans, but presidential science adviser James Killian played a key role in the decision.

[4] The four letter exchange between McCone and Stans is reprinted on pp. 12-13 of the hearings cited in the preceding footnote. In his second letter, McCone again notes "the need for your assurance that the amounts required for this project in future years would be considered entirely apart from any budgetary ceilings for

In December 1960, a joint GAC-PSAC panel chaired by Emanuel Piore took issue with the Budget Bureau doctrine of centralized agency responsibility, declaring that

High energy physics constitutes a national program which does not fall logically into the mission of a single agency. We believe that diverse support of this field through the Atomic Energy Commission, the Department of Defense (the Office of Naval Research and the Office of Scientific Research) and the National Science Foundation [is] especially useful both to high-energy physics and to the agencies concerned; we believe that this tradition should be continued. For diverse support to be successful, it is necessary that the fraction contributed by the agencies (the Department of Defense and the National Science Foundation) which now carry a smaller part of the program should be increased or at least maintained as the program expands; in particular, some of the new construction should be supported by the Department of Defense and the National Science Foundation.[5]

A similar position was adopted by the 1963 GAC-PSAC Ramsey panel on high energy accelerator physics, which noted pointedly that the advice of physicists on this matter had not been taken:

Despite the endorsement of the principle of diversity of support of earlier Panels, it appears that the AEC has, in fact, become the custodian of the national high energy physics program. Diversity of support, with the NSF and the agencies of the Department of Defense taking a

---

the remainder of the Commission's program. I feel that your letter provides little assurance in this regard. . . ." Stans' reply proffered in its second paragraph and withheld in its first the words that McCone requested:

"As you point out in your letter, the Stanford accelerator is indeed a major project both for construction and operation. Inevitably the decision to commit funds of this magnitude to the Stanford accelerator will have some effect upon the availability of funds for other governmental purposes, whether within or outside the Commission's program. In this sense we cannot, from the standpoint of sound financial management, consider this project or any other project "entirely apart" from the Government's total fiscal needs.

On the other hand, it is clearly not our intention to expect the Commission to absorb the cost of the project in its normal budget. I visualize that in arriving at annual ceilings and budget allowances, the fund requirements for this project will be considered separately and will be assigned a special priority. This should meet your point entirely." (*vide supra.*, p. 13)

[5] The Piore report is reprinted in *High Energy Physics Program: Report on National Policy and Background Information, op. cit.*, p. 129. Other members of the panel were Leland Haworth, Jesse Beams, Hans Bethe, Edwin McMillan, and Eugene Wigner.

larger share of the support than now projected, will be of benefit both to the agencies and to the science.[6]

It is significant that the Budget Bureau view was finally breached in the case of the 10-bev Cornell electron synchrotron, whose estimated $13 million construction cost came from the 1964 and 1965 budgets of the National Science Foundation.[7]

Though a majority of recent Commissions have viewed the expanding programs of high energy research with favor (three Commissioners, Seaborg, Haworth, and Tape having previously been associated with one or the other of the nation's two greatest high energy laboratories at Berkeley and Brookhaven), the Joint Committee has expressed the same concern that troubled McCone—that expenditures which may soon reach half a billion dollars a year not crowd out other nuclear programs:

What we find is that a constancy exists in the total amount of money that shows up in the AEC budget every year.

In 1964 we had $2,435 million. In 1965 $2,283 million. In 1966, $2,267 million. Now if the high-energy physics expenditures balloon as they are bound to, what we are worried about is 1967, 1968, and the same relative closeness of the figures in the AEC budget, which means that the high-energy physics program . . . is competing with the other activities of the AEC.[8]

Where, in principle, should government responsibility for the accelerators be lodged? The following reasons may be given for and against lodging it with the AEC and the National Science Foundation, respectively:

For the AEC

1. AEC staff have more experience with the construction and operation of accelerators than any other agency, and field staff at

---

[6] *Report of the Panel on High Energy Accelerator Physics of the General Advisory Committee to the Atomic Energy Commission and the President's Science Advisory Committee,* Atomic Energy Commission (April 26, 1963), p. 14.

[7] See testimony of NSF Director Leland Haworth in *Independent Offices Appropriations for 1965,* Hearings before a subcommittee of the House Appropriations Committee, 88 Cong. 2 sess. (1964), Pt. 2, p. 764.

[8] Representative Craig Hosmer in *High Energy Physics Research, op. cit.,* p. 347; see also the similar remarks of Joint Committee Chairman Holifield and Representative Melvin Price (pp. 344-47).

most sites provide important services, particularly during construction.

2. Despite minor irritations, administrative relations between the AEC and its high energy laboratories have generally been good.

3. ". . . scientific productivity under the present arrangement is outstandingly high. Why change something known to be successful for something untried?"[9]

4. Most spokesmen for high energy laboratories who expressed an opinion on the point in 1965 would prefer to remain with the AEC.

5. High energy physics *is* related to the AEC mission of dealing with the exotic forces of matter, and may some day conceivably lead to practical applications that the agency is qualified to exploit.

6. At three laboratories—Brookhaven, Argonne, and Berkeley—high energy work is closely and beneficially linked to other AEC programs.

7. The AEC and the Joint Committee have succeeded in financing and administering a great program in high energy research which is the envy of many scientists and nations.

Against the AEC

1. Monopolies are not the best way to develop any field of science.

2. AEC controls have grown to such a point that, given a free choice, many university administrators and scientists would prefer to deal with another agency (as by all, or at least some, accounts, Stanford preferred to deal with the Office of Naval Research and Cornell, with NSF).[10]

3. Under the aegis of AEC and the Joint Committee national

[9] Letter from a senior laboratory official (July 16, 1965).

[10] Cf. the charge of Raymond Woodrow, Director of Research Administration at Princeton, that "AEC contracts, particularly cost type contracts, have a much stronger flavor of making the contractor an agent of the Government in a master-servant type of relationship than is true of contracts Princeton University has received from any other federal agency." Not a direct quotation, but a paraphrase by Lawrence Caruso in his paper, "Contracting with the Atomic Energy Commission," *Atomic Energy Law Journal* (Winter 1962), p. 355.

expenditures on high energy physics have grown out of bounds—i.e., out of balance with the needs of other fields of pure science and of nuclear engineering.

4. Many representatives of industry and disinterested observers who expressed an opinion on the point in 1965 would like to see AEC relinquish its responsibilities in high energy physics, which they regard as a distraction from, and an exaction on, other worthy nuclear and scientific programs.

5. An agency whose paramount objectives are the development of new, and often classified, forms of technology is not ideally suited to administer programs of pure research, since many staff apply to the latter programs rules and experiences derived from the paramount objectives.[11]

For the NSF

1. NSF is accustomed to delegating more responsibility to, and imposing fewer controls on universities than is the AEC.

2. A larger role for NSF in government basic research programs has been advocated by recent presidents, the National Academy of Sciences, and countless spokesmen for academic science.

3. Several GAC-PSAC panels have advocated that the NSF's responsibilities and expenditures in high energy physics be increased.

4. NSF has been established explicitly to promote education and research in all fields of basic science, of which high energy physics is one.

---

[11] An example is Harvard's two year negotiations to get the AEC to modify its normal security regulations to fit the circumstances of unclassified research at the Cambridge accelerator:

"The philosophic point at issue was whether national security required the same application of secrecy to peaceful atomic research as to weapons and military research. . . . The AEC wanted the right of prior approval on employment of aliens, whether friendly or hostile, at the accelerator. . . . The AEC also wanted to restrict visits to the accelerator by scientists from Soviet bloc countries and wanted to impose limitations on the release of data compiled from experiments at the facility. . . . The AEC also wanted Harvard to censor and regulate accelerator-connected correspondence of its scientists with foreigners so that Harvard could be sure that the U.S. received as much intelligence from other countries as Harvard's scientists revealed." Cal Brumley, "Harvard Talks Back," *Wall Street Journal* (July 3, 1963), p. 10.

5. As its responsibilities include the entire spectrum of science, NSF is better able than the AEC to achieve an equitable balance in federal expenditures for different fields of pure science.

Against the NSF

1. NSF has had little experience with the construction or operation of large laboratories, and "its largest single project to date, Mohole, is, to put it delicately, not pointed to as a bright star in the firmament of American science."[12]

2. NSF does not have the scientific or administrative staff qualified to handle the special technical problems of major accelerators.

3. Because its congressional committees are not as strong as the Joint Committee, there is more danger that high energy physics will founder under NSF auspices, and the large expenditures involved could swamp and imbalance an agency whose 1966 appropriation was only $480 million.

Of all the pros and cons summarized above, it is evident that money, at hand and in mind, is most important. Some (not all) who like the idea of transferring accelerators from the AEC to NSF are either hostile or indifferent to the future of high energy physics, and feel that it has drawn from the public purse sums better devoted to other public programs. A good many faculty, of course, are simply prejudiced against the AEC, because it makes bombs, and for the NSF, because it does not.

Those opposing the transfer do so primarily on the grounds of realistic politics. Rather than attempting to paraphrase their views, let us quote extensively from statements of two physicists, respected and influential spokesmen for both pure science and high energy physics, and intimately familiar with both the AEC and the NSF. One wrote:

The budget for these [high energy] laboratories is greater than the entire budget for the National Science Foundation (for fiscal 1965) and this, therefore, would throw a tremendous burden of management on the NSF for which it could not easily or quickly prepare itself. Furthermore, the present House Independent Offices Appropriations Sub-

[12] Same letter cited in footnote 9.

committee has been very slow to recognize the growing responsibilities and budget needs of NSF and a sudden doubling of its budget would probably be strongly resisted by this committee. The net result might be that, since the activities of the nuclear laboratories could not be easily cut, the entire basic-research program of the Foundation might be seriously endangered. Basic nuclear physics research properly belongs in the AEC. It is only a modest part of their budget, and is supported by the Joint Committee. I would strongly oppose for many reasons, a switch in responsibilities. Either the nuclear laboratories or the rest of the NSF program or both might be disastrously affected.[13]

The second physicist was also concerned about money, but appeared more open-minded about the possible desirability of transferring at least some accelerators to NSF at a later date:

As a practical matter the budget of the NSF has had to grow very rapidly during the last few years primarily due to the addition of responsibilities in science education and in the creation of new research centers. Since Congress views an abnormally high rate of growth with alarm it would be unrealistic to assume that the Congress would approve transfer of large basic research responsibility from the mission-oriented agencies to the NSF in addition to its other growing activities. Moreover, there is value in itself to maintain the intimate contact of the mission-oriented agencies with basic research and to persuade them that they must share in the responsibility for the support of science in the country.

The Science Foundation is supporting the 10 BeV Cornell Electron Accelerator. This will provide an important test case, both of the NSF's ability to monitor an activity of this kind and as an important comparison of how a program of this magnitude can be carried out with very much less administrative paper work than is practiced by the AEC. I feel that transfer of the large basic research facilities of the AEC to the NSF should be approached with caution pending the outcome of the Cornell experience. I suggest this both for the reasons given above and noting that NSF management of large research activities has been notably unsuccessful in instances such as the large radio telescope in West Virginia and the Mohole where the NSF attempted to manage directly a large, scientific construction project....[14]

[13] Letter, August 11, 1965.
[14] Letter, July 13, 1965.

Our final conclusion does not differ radically from that of the latter physicist. Clearly, NSF has shown weaknesses in managing large projects, which should be corrected. Although the AEC is far more experienced, it is not without its own management faults. The errors of NSF have been in the direction of under-management, and those of AEC, of over-management; and if either error *must* be committed, the former is better suited to the operational and the latter to the construction stages of a basic research facility.

On balance, we believe that a strong case can be made for the early transfer to NSF of at any rate two of the smaller AEC-funded accelerators, at Cambridge and Princeton.[15] If all goes well with these and with the Cornell machine, the very much larger Stanford installation (which would then be operational) might follow, in due course. The assignment of the 200-bev should be determined in the light of the conditions prevailing when, and if, it comes into operation. Berkeley and Brookhaven, being more closely tied to the structure and history of the Commission, may better be left to share and to contribute to its destiny.

---

[15] If we read his testimony correctly, I. I. Rabi has advocated a not dissimilar course:

"I like to see the Science Foundation play a role in the high energy field. . . . I think they have done an excellent job in the support of radio astronomy and visual astronomy in the form of large national laboratories . . . and I would like to see them enter the [high energy] field in a very big way. . . .

". . . I certainly would not suggest anything drastic to be done immediately, because an organization has to be built up so it can handle these matters, and what I am talking about involves a large amount of money. . . . by starting in some subject in a cooperative way . . . with the Atomic Energy Commission, then there could gradually be the shift over of some projects into the National Science Foundation. . . . There have been large cyclotrons which were started at one agency and then became a cooperative project and then went on over to another agency in the end. It was a question of funding and which agency would have the most appropriate interest. This I would suggest would be the direction in which the National Science Foundation should get into things to get its feet wet. First, it has to have some money so as to contribute. In this way they will acquire the management skills necessary for that project, the staff, and ultimately they might take over some of them. I wouldn't suggest it is something which should happen overnight or in 1 year." *Government and Science, Review of the National Science Foundation,* Hearings before the Subcommittee on Science, Research, and Development of the House Science and Astronautics Committee, 89 Cong. 1 sess. (1965), Vol. I, pp. 345, 351.

The Future Mission of the Laboratories— and the AEC

The agency established in 1946 primarily to develop and manufacture more and better nuclear bombs has done just that; the goal of developing economic civilian nuclear power reactors, given a special stimulus by the 1954 legislation, has also largely been achieved. As the major objectives set by its two major statutes have thus been virtually realized, the AEC is passing through a visible climacteric of spirit and purpose. Thus, AEC Chairman Seaborg sounds the same note as some critics, that "the AEC is one Government agency which is in the unique position of slowly working itself out of a job." He does not, to be sure, proceed to their conclusion that the agency should, therefore, be dismembered and its functions and facilities bequeathed to tributary agencies and private industry, but hastens to add that "new applications of nuclear energy demand that the AEC take on new jobs in other areas."[16]

Three basic courses are open for the AEC:

Continuing Along Present Lines

"Present lines" may be defined as pushing all programs of nuclear science and technology that the Congress, the President, and the President's budget will sanction, as well as those non-nuclear programs that can be cultivated without jeopardizing the status of nuclear work.

Weapons improvement will be pressed as hard as ideas, budgets, and treaties permit; and a breakdown in the treaty banning atmospheric tests or a breakthrough in the development of anti-missile missiles, or some other revolutionary device, might give it a decided boost. However, should the current treaty remain in force, and perhaps be extended to underground tests (or those above a certain size), the diversification of work at the weapons laboratories can be expected to continue. For the AEC as a whole, the

[16] Glenn Seaborg, "Nuclear Power Comes of Age," remarks, Edison Electric Institute Convention, Miami Beach (May 4, 1965), reprinted in *Congressional Record*, daily edition (May 5, 1965), p. 9276.

most likely prospect is a relative growth in expenditures for civilian nuclear technology and basic research.

In this view, which currently appears dominant within the Commission, the main obstacles to such growth and to the future vitality of AEC programs are budgetary (or political), not intrinsic or statutory. As one reader put it, ". . . the present charter is almost limitless, and—unless competed for by other governmental divisions—the Commission can do almost everything for which they can get appropriations."

Dismemberment

A surprising number of observers believe that the best thing that might now be done with the AEC is to disband it. "If its job is approaching completion, why not let it fade out?" asks an industrial executive. "It would establish a new milestone for democracy. . . ." According to this view, the basic principle of establishing a special agency and congressional committee to handle nuclear affairs is now outmoded and disrupts the normal play of economic and political forces. A more balanced allocation and a more rational choice among alternative technologies and sciences would result if nuclear weapons programs were transferred to the Department of Defense, naval reactor programs to the Navy, maritime reactors to the Maritime Administration, nuclear space propulsion to NASA, physical research to the National Science Foundation, biological research to the National Institutes of Health, and so on. AEC's significant regulatory functions could be preserved either by setting up its Licensing and Regulatory Divisions as an independent agency, or transferring their functions and personnel to such bodies as the Federal Power Commission and the Public Health Service.

In this reallocation of responsibilities, many AEC plants and laboratories would survive intact, but others might be segmented or put on the block and sold to the highest (public or private) bidder. The segmentation of, and introduction of private capital into, the Hanford operation affords some insight into how such a disposition might be undertaken.

Few who advocate the foregoing course expect it to be adopted, the invariable reason being that although some Commissioners and some President might conceivably advocate it, the fearsome Joint Committee is unlikely to abolish itself.

Revising the Charter

The AEC's first charter, drafted under the scorching impress of the only two nuclear bombs yet used in earnest, lasted eight years; its second has already lasted twelve. No harm and much good can come from a fresh attempt to define what the nation should expect of its nuclear authorities and facilities during the next twelve years. Such an attempt might be just as likely to enlarge as to reduce the functions of the AEC and its laboratories.

Foreseeing in 1955 that the AEC laboratories might work themselves out of their nuclear missions, Alvin Weinberg speculated on what other national objectives might be assigned to them. He suggested three: the development of energy sources other than uranium and fossil fuels; finding better ways of producing food and water supplies; and "geological engineering" to enable the earth better to sustain its increasing population:

. . . after all, these laboratories are designated national, not atomic energy, laboratories, and this broader name is really an accurate description of their tremendous capacity.

. . . when it becomes desirable for them to branch out into other fields may require considerable administrative reshuffling. For example, I have heard it suggested that eventually the Atomic Energy Commission might be renamed simply the Energy Commission, with all that such a renaming would imply.

I suppose one could go further and think eventually of a "natural resources," or perhaps "geologic engineering," commission to take responsibility for these long term environmental problems which we hope are tractable to large scale project research.[17]

One need not accept any of Weinberg's specific prescriptions to acknowledge that he early recognized a problem that will not go away by being ignored, and which warrants full and open public discussion. Of course, the AEC laboratories can continue to dream up and develop exotic forms of nuclear technology, but is that the best use that can be made at this juncture of their great talents

[17] Alvin Weinberg, "Future Aims of Large Scale Research," *Chemical and Engineering News* (May 23, 1955), p. 2191.

and resources? Is it beyond our political ability to redefine their technical and scientific objectives?[18]

Those who despair of doing so point simply to the Joint Committee, as if it were an immobile monolith of power-mad men, rather than a group of unusually able, experienced, and realistic congressmen; and realistic congressmen are, above all, movable and adaptable men.

It is no secret that a good many persons and some recent presidents would have liked to abolish the Joint Committee,[19] but they have been unable to find a formula for doing so. This is sheer speculation, but is it impossible to conceive of an accommodation under which the scope of the AEC is *broadened* (into, let us say, an Energy Development Agency) and, in exchange for this enlargement of its powers, the Joint Committee is bifurcated and recon-

---

[18] Harvey Brooks, chairman of the Committee on Science and Public Policy of the National Academy of Sciences, has made a similar plea in a recent address. "The range of technological capabilities represented by these laboratories [i.e., major national laboratories such as those of the AEC] . . . is extraordinary, but after a few years, the magnificent machinery tends to get devoted to less and less significant problems and it is extremely difficult to redefine their missions in response to the changing goals of federal science. . . . We do not treat our federal laboratories as a common national resource to be used flexibly for many of the purposes of government. Rather we tend to regard each laboratory as the inviolate preserve of the agency to which it belongs. . . . I feel it is time we learned how to use these institutions more flexibly for national purposes with less worry about roles and missions." Extract from a talk given in Oklahoma City in October 1966, as reported in *Science*, November 4, 1966, p. 620.

[19] The head of one AEC installation is said to have expostulated that "the Joint Committee is unconstitutional" (the same thing was said, in its time, about Boulder Dam), and President Eisenhower's parting advice to President-Elect Kennedy included an account of his frustrations with the Joint Committee that concluded, "Frankly, I see no need for the continuance of the Joint Committee on Atomic Energy." Dwight D. Eisenhower, *Waging Peace, 1956-1961; the White House Years* (Garden City, New York, Doubleday & Co., 1965), p. 715.

Joint Committee Chairman Chet Holifield has acknowledged and replied to such charges: "It has also been suggested by some that the committee on occasion has encroached on the doctrine and practice of separation of powers; that what the committee regards as its proper role in policymaking functions is in fact an assault on executive powers. I could dismiss this charge by simply noting that the Constitution contemplates coequal branches of government, not domination by one—the executive—over the other. But I cannot resist pointing out also the irony of the charge, coming as it does from some of the same critics who chastise Congress as a whole for not resisting the trend toward executive erosion of legislative power." *Congressional Record*, daily edition (August 2, 1966), p. 17079.

stituted to include representatives of conventional fuel areas, while
the AEC, in turn, is bifurcated into a regulatory commission and
an operating agency with a single administrator?

We cannot presume to say which of the foregoing, or which additional, courses the nation should adopt, but there is a widespread conviction among private citizens immersed in nuclear
affairs that the first—continuing along present lines—is inadequate
or, at least, cannot be accepted as adequate until it has been subjected to critical public scrutiny and *shown* to be adequate. "What
is evident," declares one reader, "is that . . . all aspects of [the
AEC charter] . . . are in dire need of extensive public and private
discussion." We agree.

Index

Hanford

Idaho Falls

Berkeley
Livermore
Stanford
Jackass Flats
Mercury

Canoga Park

Rocky Flats

Hal

Los Alamos
Sandia
S. Albuquerque

Pantex

Mea

- Laboratory
- Production
- Testing Station
- Power Reactor
- Laboratory & Production
- Laboratory & Testing Station